SCRIBNER READING SERIES

EACH NEW DAY

Jack Cassidy

Doris Roettger   *Karen K. Wixson*

SCRIBNER EDUCATIONAL PUBLISHERS
New York

ACKNOWLEDGMENTS

"The Baker's Cat" is from "The Baker's Cat" by Joan Aiken from A NECKLACE OF RAINDROPS AND OTHER STORIES. Copyright © 1968 by Joan Aiken. Reprinted by permission of Doubleday & Company, Inc., the author and Jonathan Cape Ltd.

"The Case of the Broken Window" is adapted from ENCYCLOPEDIA BROWN AND THE CASE OF THE DEAD EAGLES by Donald J. Sobol. Text Copyright © 1975 by Donald J. Sobol. Reprinted by permission of E. P. Dutton, a division of New American Library. By permission also of McIntosh & Otis, Inc.

"Chin Chiang and the Dragon's Dance" adapted from CHIN CHIANG AND THE DRAGON'S DANCE by Ian Wallace. Text Copyright © 1985 by Ian Wallace. (A Margaret K. McElderry Book.) Reprinted with the permission of Atheneum Publishers and the author.

"Count on Your Fingers African Style" is abridged and adapted from COUNT ON YOUR FINGERS AFRICAN STYLE by Claudia Zaslavsky. (Thomas Y. Crowell Company) Copyright © 1980 by Claudia Zaslavsky. Reprinted by permission of Harper & Row, Publishers, Inc.

"Daniel's Duck" is adapted from DANIEL'S DUCK by Clyde Robert Bulla. Text Copyright © 1980 by Clyde Robert Bulla. Reprinted by permission of Harper & Row, Publishers, Inc. and Bill Berger Associates.

"Everything Off the Floor!" is from MAURICE'S ROOM by Paula Fox. Copyright © 1966 by Paula Fox. Edited with permission of Macmillan Publishing Company and Lescher & Lescher, Ltd.

"Finger Multiplication" is from "Finger Multiplication" by Linda Olsen George which appeared originally in *Cricket* Magazine. Copyright © 1984 by Linda Olsen George and reprinted with her permission.

"Grizzly Bear" is from THE CHILDREN SING IN THE FAR WEST by Mary Austin. Copyright © 1928 by Mary Austin. Copyright renewed 1956 by Kenneth M. Chapman and Mary C. Wheelwright. Reprinted by permission of Houghton Mifflin Company.

"The Grizzly Bear with the Golden Ears" is an adaptation of the entire text of THE GRIZZLY BEAR WITH THE GOLDEN EARS by Jean Craighead George. Copyright © 1982 by Jean Craighead George. Reprinted by permission of Harper & Row, Publishers, Inc. and Curtis Brown, Ltd.

(Acknowledgments continued on page 317)

SCRIBNER EDUCATIONAL PUBLISHERS
866 Third Avenue
New York, NY 10022
Collier Macmillan Publishers, London
Collier Macmillan Canada, Inc.

Printed in the United States of America

ISBN 0-02-256090-4

9 8 7 6 5 4 3 2

EACH
NEW DAY

Contents

5

STRATEGIES
TO USE WHEN YOU MEET A NEW WORD

SAY THE WORD.
Is it a word you know?
Is it a word you have heard other people use?

LOOK AT THE WORD.
Is it a compound word? Do you know the meanings of the smaller words?
Are any parts of the word like another word you know? Does it have a familiar base word? Does it have a familiar prefix or suffix?

READ THE SENTENCE IN WHICH THE WORD APPEARS.
Are there any clues that help you understand the meaning of the new word?

If you are still not sure what the word means, look it up in the glossary or a dictionary to find out its meaning.

STRATEGIES
TO USE WHEN YOU WRITE

PREWRITING—Before you write,
- choose a topic, something you want to write about.
- think about who will read what you write.
- make notes on what you want to write about.

WRITING—When you write,
- use your notes to put your ideas together.
- write a topic sentence that tells the main idea.
- write some sentences that tell more about the main idea.

REVISING—After you write,
- read what you wrote.
- edit it. Make sure it makes sense and says what you want it to say.
- proofread it. Make sure your spelling and punctuation marks are correct.

Use these marks when you edit and proofread.		
	¶	Start new paragraph
	∧	Add this
	ℓ	Take this out
	lowercase	Make this lowercase
	capital	Make this uppercase

- copy your work on a clean sheet of paper.

1

PET PROBLEMS

There are three kinds of people. There are people who don't have pets. There are people who do have pets. And there are people who don't have a pet but want one. Which kind of person are you?

If you don't have a pet, you are missing one of the great joys of life. If you do have a pet, then you know that pets and people sometimes cause each other problems. If you want a pet but don't have one, this unit will help you decide which pet is right for you.

As you read this unit, think about how some pets cause problems for people. Also think about how some people *cause problems for* pets.

Mog is a playful but gentle cat. He becomes a giant-sized pet problem for Mrs. Jones, though, when he grows as big as a house.

What does Mog like that most cats do not like? Why does Mog grow so big?

The Baker's Cat

by JOAN AIKEN

Once there was an old lady, Mrs. Jones, who lived with her cat, Mog. Mrs. Jones kept a baker's shop in a little tiny town at the bottom of a valley between two mountains.

Every morning you could see Mrs. Jones's light twinkle on, long before all the other houses in the town, because she got up very early to bake loaves and buns and jam tarts and cakes.

First thing in the morning, Mrs. Jones lit a big fire. Then she made dough out of water and sugar and yeast. Then she put the dough into pans and set it in front of the fire to rise.

Mog got up early, too. *He* got up to catch mice. When he had chased all the mice out of the bakery, he wanted to sit in front of the warm fire. But Mrs. Jones wouldn't let him, because of the loaves and buns there, rising in their pans.

She said, "Don't sit on the buns, Mog."

The buns were rising nicely. They were getting fine and big. That is what yeast does. It makes bread and buns and cakes swell up and get bigger and bigger.

Since Mog was not allowed to sit by the fire, he went to play in the sink.

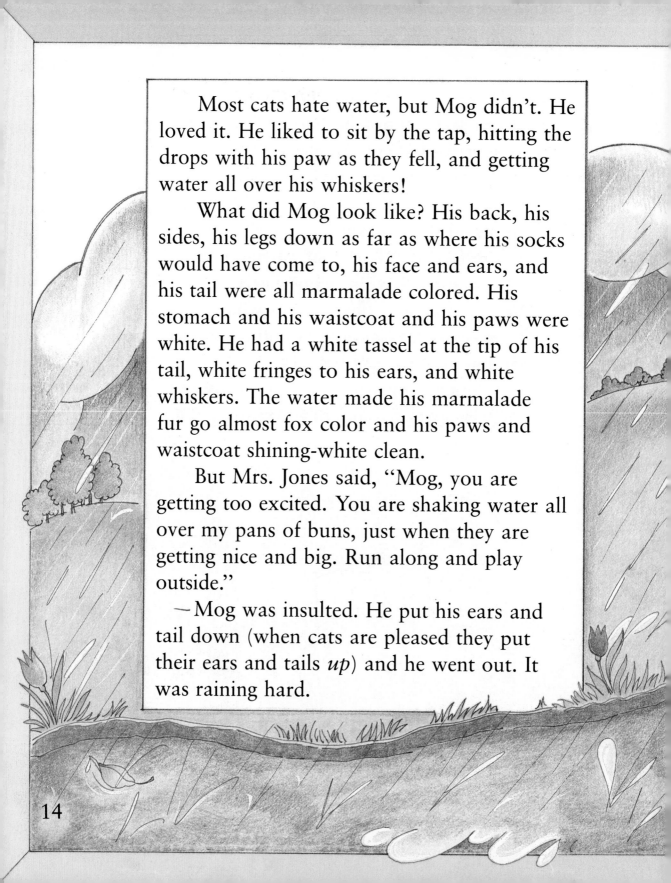

Most cats hate water, but Mog didn't. He loved it. He liked to sit by the tap, hitting the drops with his paw as they fell, and getting water all over his whiskers!

What did Mog look like? His back, his sides, his legs down as far as where his socks would have come to, his face and ears, and his tail were all marmalade colored. His stomach and his waistcoat and his paws were white. He had a white tassel at the tip of his tail, white fringes to his ears, and white whiskers. The water made his marmalade fur go almost fox color and his paws and waistcoat shining-white clean.

But Mrs. Jones said, "Mog, you are getting too excited. You are shaking water all over my pans of buns, just when they are getting nice and big. Run along and play outside."

—Mog was insulted. He put his ears and tail down (when cats are pleased they put their ears and tails *up*) and he went out. It was raining hard.

A rushing river ran through the middle of the town. Mog went and sat *in* the water and looked for fish. But there were no fish in that part of the river. Mog got wetter and wetter. But he didn't care. Soon he began to sneeze.

Then Mrs. Jones opened her door and called, "Mog! I have put the buns in the oven. You can come in now and sit by the fire."

Mog was so wet that he was shiny all over. As he sat by the fire, he sneezed nine times.

Mrs. Jones said, "Oh dear, Mog, are you catching a cold?"

She dried him with a towel and gave him some warm milk with yeast in it. Yeast is good for people when they are feeling poorly.

Then she left him sitting in front of the fire and began making jam tarts. When she had put the tarts in the oven, she went out shopping, taking her umbrella.

But what do you think was happening to Mog?

The yeast was making him rise.

As he sat dozing in front of the lovely warm fire, he was growing bigger and bigger.

First he grew as big as a sheep.

Then he grew as big as a donkey.

Then he grew as big as a horse.

Then he grew as big as a hippopotamus.

By now he was too big for Mrs. Jones's little kitchen, but he was far too big to get through the door. He just burst the walls.

When Mrs. Jones came home with her shopping bag and her umbrella, she cried out, "Mercy me, what is happening to my house?"

The whole house was bulging. It was swaying. Huge whiskers were poking out of the kitchen window. A marmalade-colored tail came out of the door. A white paw came out of one bedroom window, and an ear with a white fringe out of the other.

"Morow?" said Mog. He was waking up from his nap and trying to stretch.

Then the whole house fell down.

"Oh, Mog!" cried Mrs. Jones. "*Look* what you've done."

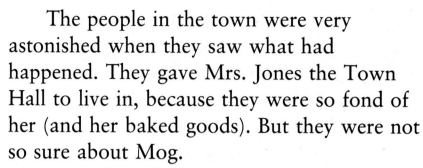

The people in the town were very astonished when they saw what had happened. They gave Mrs. Jones the Town Hall to live in, because they were so fond of her (and her baked goods). But they were not so sure about Mog.

The Mayor said, "Suppose he goes on growing and breaks our Town Hall? Suppose he turns fierce? It would not be safe to have him in the town. He is too big."

Mrs. Jones said, "Mog is a gentle cat. He would not hurt anybody."

"We will wait and see about that," said the Mayor. "Suppose he sat down on someone? Suppose he was hungry? What will he eat? He had better live outside the town, up on the mountain."

18

So everyone shouted, "Shoo! Scram! Pssst! Shoo!" and poor Mog was driven outside the town gates. It was still raining hard. Water was rushing down the mountains. Not that Mog cared.

But poor Mrs. Jones was very sad. She began making a new lot of loaves and buns in the Town Hall, crying into the dough so much that it was too wet and very salty.

Mog walked up the valley between the two mountains. By now he was bigger than an elephant—almost as big as a whale! When the sheep on the mountain saw him coming, they were scared to death and galloped away. But he took no notice of them. He was looking for fish in the river. He caught lots of fish! He was having a fine time.

By now it had been raining for so long that Mog heard a loud, watery roar at the top of the valley. He saw a huge wall of water coming toward him. The river was beginning to flood as more and more rainwater poured down into it, off the mountains.

Mog thought, "If I don't stop that water, all these fine fish will be washed away."

So he sat down, plump in the middle of the valley, and he spread himself out like a big, fat cottage loaf.

The water could not get by.

The people in the town had heard the roar of the flood-water. They were very frightened. The Mayor shouted, "Run up the mountains before the water gets to the town, or we shall all be drowned!"

So they all rushed up the mountains, some on one side of the town, some on the other.

What did they see then?

Why, Mog sitting in the middle of the valley. Beyond him was a great lake.

"Mrs. Jones," said the Mayor, "can you make your cat stay there till we have built a dam across the valley, to keep all that water back?"

"I will try," said Mrs. Jones. "He mostly sits still if he is tickled under his chin."

So for three days, everybody in the town took turns tickling Mog under his chin with hay rakes. He purred and purred and purred. His purring made big waves roll right across the lake of flood-water.

All this time, the best builders were making a great dam across the valley.

People brought Mog all sorts of nice things to eat, too—bowls of cream, milk, and tuna. But he was not very hungry. He had eaten so much fish.

On the third day, they finished the dam. The town was safe.

The Mayor said, "I see now that Mog is a gentle cat. He can live in the Town Hall with you, Mrs. Jones. Here is a badge for him to wear."

The badge was on a silver chain to go round his neck. It said MOG SAVED OUR TOWN.

TOWN HALL

MOG
SAVED OUR TOWN

22

So Mrs. Jones and Mog have lived happily ever after in the Town Hall. If you should go to the little town of Carnmog, you may see the police officer holding up the traffic while Mog walks through the streets on his way to catch fish in the lake for breakfast. His tail waves above the houses and his whiskers rattle against the upstairs windows. But people know he will not hurt them, because he is a gentle cat.

He loves to play in the lake, and sometimes he gets so wet that he sneezes. But Mrs. Jones is not going to give him any more yeast.

He is quite big enough already!

CHECK FOR UNDERSTANDING

1. What did Mog like that most cats do not like?
2. Why did Mog grow so big?
3. What was Mog's reason for stopping the flood-water coming down the mountain?
4. Did the townspeople think Mog stopped the water to save them? Explain why you think they did or didn't.

Consonant Clusters

Say the words blue balloon. Do you hear the difference in the way the words begin? In balloon you hear a vowel sound between b and l. There is no vowel between b and l in blue. Blue begins with a consonant cluster. Two or more consonant letters and sounds together in a word are called a **consonant cluster.**

Read the list of words below. Look for a consonant cluster at the beginning of each word.

blow	broke	clip	snow	spray
bring	class	small	spell	string

How many different consonant clusters did you find? You should have found eight. They are bl, br, cl, sm, sn, sp, spr, and str. Some other consonant clusters are cr, dr, fl, pr, sw, st, and tr.

Sometimes three consonant letters form a cluster, such as the letters spr in spring. Say the word spring and listen to the sounds made by the consonant letters s, p, and r together.

Look again at the list of words on page 24. Find the words that begin with the same consonant cluster as brown. Now find words beginning with the same cluster as clown. Can you think of any other words that begin with a three-letter cluster, such as spray and string?

Consonant clusters sometimes come at the end of words. Say the word gold. Do you hear the sounds of the consonants l and d together? These two consonant letters form the consonant cluster ld, which is only found at the end of a word or syllable.

Read the words below. You should find eight different consonant clusters.

bald	elf	stomp	disk	storm
gold	self	dump	ask	harm
held	milk	stamp	task	horn
wild	silk	risk	warm	torn

Start starts and ends with a consonant cluster. There is a consonant cluster at the end of end. How many more consonant clusters can you find in the two sentences you just read?

PARAKEETS and PEACH PIES

by KAY SMITH

Sometimes it is not a pet's size that causes problems. Sometimes it is the number of pets. When Matthew's mother has people visiting, too many pets cause too many problems.

What does Matthew find inside the house when he gets home from school? Why doesn't Matthew want to finish the question he started to ask his mother?

When Matthew came home from school, he saw his mother sitting on the porch steps.

"Mom! Mom!" he called, running up the path. "I have to ask you something right away!"

"Just a minute," Mother said. "I want to show you something first."

26

Matthew followed his mother into the house. "Hey!" he cried. "The hall's a mess!"

The dining room was worse.

And after one look at the living room, Matthew gasped, "What happened to our house?"

Mother sat down on the sofa and gave a big sigh.

"Well," she said, "today the Ladies' Literary League met here for lunch and . . . your parakeet perched on Mrs. Parker's piece of peach pie and pecked at the pastry.

"Your kitten climbed up on the corner cabinet and crashed into Mrs. Carter's coffee cup.

"Mrs. French found your frog in her favorite hat—and fainted.

"Your dog dragged in all of Dad's dirty dungarees and dumped them in the dining room doorway.

"Your snake scared Mrs. Smith so, that she showered shrimp salad all over our satin sofa.

"Your hamster had her babies inside Mrs. Higgins' hand-beaded handbag.

"Your lizard leaped on Mrs. Lester's leg, and her lunch landed in her lap.

"The fishbowl fell over, and your fantails flopped into Mrs. Franklin's fruit punch.

"Your rabbits ran right through the room and ruined Mrs. Richard's report on *Restful Reading.*

"Your parrot screamed, 'PIPE DOWN, PEST!' all during poor Mrs. Pepper's poetry.

"Your chickens chased our charming Books-for-Children chairperson around the chinaberry tree."

Mother leaned back and gave another sigh. "I don't think the Ladies' Literary League will ever feel brave enough to have lunch at our house again."

"I'm so sorry, Mom. Listen, I'll clean up. I'll do anything!"

29

"All right, Matthew. But first, please put your pets in a safe place. Once is enough."

Matthew collected his pets and started to leave. Mother stopped him. "Wait, Matthew. What was it you wanted to ask me when you first came home?"

"Never mind, Mom . . ."

"Matthew," Mother insisted, "go ahead and ask. I'm not angry with you—just a little upset."

Matthew shook his head sadly.

"Oh, for heaven's sake, Matthew. Ask me!"

Matthew took a very deep breath. "Michael Myer's mouse has had more babies. May I have a mouse, Mom?"

30

CHECK FOR UNDERSTANDING

1. What did Matthew find when he got home from school?
2. Which animal perched on Mrs. Parker's peach pie, and what did it do to the pie?
3. Which animal screamed during Mrs. Pepper's poetry reading, and what did it say?
4. Why didn't Matthew want to finish the question he started to ask his mother?

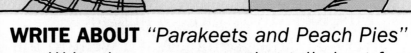

WRITE ABOUT *"Parakeets and Peach Pies"*
Write three sentences that tell about funny problems zoo animals might get into. You could write about these animals: a tiger, a kangaroo, a panda, or a monkey. In each sentence use some words that begin with the same sound as the animal's name.

31

THE ROOSTER WHO UNDERSTOOD JAPANESE

by YOSHIKO UCHIDA

Miyo's friend, Mrs. K., has a rooster named Mr. Lincoln. Mrs. K. thinks Mr. Lincoln is a wonderful pet. But her new neighbor thinks he is a problem.

Why does the neighbor get angry about Mr. Lincoln? How does Miyo solve Mrs. K.'s problem?

"Mrs. K!" Miyo called. "I'm here!"

Every day after school, Miyo went to the home of her neighbor, Mrs. Kitamura, whom she called "Mrs. K." Miyo's mother was a doctor at the hospital. She did not get home until supper time. So Miyo just stayed with Mrs. K. until then.

32

It was a fine arrangement all around. Mrs. K. had come to America to live after her husband died. She enjoyed Miyo's company. Not that Mrs. K. was lonely! She had a pet rooster named Mr. Lincoln. She often talked to him in Japanese.

When Miyo came home from school, Mrs. K. was usually out in her garden. But today she was nowhere to be seen.

Miyo stopped to see Mr. Lincoln. He was strutting about his pen, making rooster-like sounds. Mrs. K. had told Miyo that he understood both English and Japanese.

"Mrs. Kitamura, *doko*?" Miyo said, asking Mr. Lincoln where Mrs. K. was.

He cocked his head, looked at her, and squawked loudly.

33

Miyo shrugged. Maybe Mr. Lincoln did understand Japanese. But it certainly did not help her, because she could not understand what he said back to her.

"Never mind," she said. "I'll find her." And she hurried into Mrs. K.'s house.

"Mrs. K., I'm here!" Miyo called again.

She went through the swinging doors into the dining room. There was Mrs. K. still wearing her floppy gardening hat. She was doing something Miyo had never seen her do before. She was making herself a cup of Japanese tea. With a bamboo whisk, she was whipping up the special powdered green tea in a beautiful tea bowl.

Miyo had once seen a lady in a silk kimono perform the Japanese tea ceremony. Somehow, Mrs. K. did not look quite right preparing tea in her floppy hat. Furthermore, she was frowning. Miyo knew the tea ceremony was supposed to make one feel peaceful.

"*Mah*," Mrs. K. said, looking startled. "I was so busy with my thoughts, I didn't even hear you come in. I made some tea to calm myself. I am most upset."

"Why?" Miyo asked. Usually Mrs. K. was full of fun. But today she scarcely smiled at all.

"It's my new neighbor, Mr. Wickett," Mrs. K. said. "He is angry because he hears Mr. Lincoln crowing at six in the morning. He said that Mr. Lincoln must stop waking him up, or he is going to report me to the police for disturbing the peace."

"That's mean!" said Miyo. "You can't just tell Mr. Lincoln not to crow anymore."

"Of course not," Mrs. K. agreed. "He is only behaving in his natural rooster-like way. What am I going to do?"

Miyo wondered what she could do to help Mrs. K. Finally she said, "I'll ask my mother. She'll think of something."

Mrs. K. nodded. "I hope so," she said sadly. "In the meantime, I'll keep Mr. Lincoln in the house."

When Miyo got home, she quickly told Mother about Mr. Wickett's complaint. "It's not fair," she said, frowning. "Mr. Lincoln doesn't hurt anyone."

But Mother said, "Well, I can see Mr. Wickett's side, too. If I could sleep late, I wouldn't like having a rooster wake me at six o'clock. Besides," she added, "our town is growing. We're in the city limits now. Mrs. K. might have to give Mr. Lincoln away."

Miyo did not even want to think of such a thing. "But he's not just any old rooster," she objected. "Mrs. K. has raised him since he was a baby chick."

Mother nodded. "I know," she said. "Well, maybe we can think of something."

But nobody could—not Mother, not Miyo, not Mrs. K.

That first night, Mrs. K. brought Mr. Lincoln inside the house. She put him into a big box in her bedroom. During the night, Mr. Lincoln poked his way out of the box. By the time Mrs. K. heard him, he had scratched the floors and pecked at her sofa.

"Poor Mr. Lincoln," Mrs. K. said to Miyo the next day. "He hated being in the box. And he crowed in the morning anyway."

"I guess that keeping him inside is not the answer," said Miyo.

Mrs. K. sighed. "I suppose I'll have to give Mr. Lincoln away," she murmured sadly. "But I can't give him to just anybody. It has to be someone who will love him."

Miyo wondered how to find the right person to take Mr. Lincoln. Then, suddenly, she had an idea.

"I know," she said brightly. "I'll put an ad in our class newspaper.

Miyo's class newspaper was almost ready to be printed for the month. There were several sections—news, stories, science, sports, book reviews. At the back there was a small section of ads. That is where Miyo thought Mr. Lincoln would fit nicely.

She made her ad very special. She wrote,

"WANTED: NICE HOME FOR FRIENDLY ROOSTER. P.S. HE UNDERSTANDS JAPANESE." THEN SHE ADDED, "PLEASE HURRY. URGENT."

Miyo included her phone number. She also drew a picture of Mr. Lincoln, trying to make him look friendly.

The newspaper came out on Friday. Miyo was proud of her ad. But no one seemed at all interested in Mr. Lincoln. Instead, many people told her how much they liked her story about Mr. Botts, the school custodian. He was retiring soon.

She had written, "Say good-by to the best custodian our school ever had. Mr. Botts is retiring, and he and Mrs. Botts are going to Far Creek. They plan to grow vegetables and raise chickens. So long, Mr. Botts, and good luck."

On her way home, Miyo ran into Mr. Botts himself. He thanked her for writing the story about him.

When Mr. Botts got home that night, he read the class newspaper from cover to cover. On the last page, he saw Miyo's ad about Mr. Lincoln.

"Tami!" he called to Mrs. Botts, who happened to be Japanese. "How would you like to have a rooster that understands Japanese?"

Mrs. Botts just laughed. But Mr. Botts kept right on talking.

"We'll need a rooster for the farm when we move to Far Creek," he said. "Well, we might as well have one that understands Japanese." He showed the ad to Mrs. Botts. Then he went to the telephone to call Miyo.

"We'll take that rooster you want to find a home for," he told Miyo. "My wife could talk to it in Japanese."

Miyo could not believe it. The ad had worked. Mr. Lincoln would have a nice home with Mr. and Mrs. Botts. She ran over to tell Mrs. K. the good news.

Mrs. K. was about to stuff Mr. Lincoln into a wooden crate for the night. Quickly, Miyo told her about Mr. and Mrs. Botts. Mrs. K. gave her such a hug that she almost squeezed the breath out of her.

"Hooray! *Banzai!*" Mrs. K. said happily. "Tomorrow we will have a party to celebrate. I shall even invite Mr. Wickett," she said with a smile. "I suppose he was right. A rooster should live in the country, where nobody will care if he crows at the sun."

Mr. Wickett was a little embarrassed to come to Mrs. K.'s party. He brought a basket of fruit. "I'm sorry I caused such a commotion," he said.

But Mrs. K. told him he should not be sorry. "Life needs a little stirring up now and then," she admitted. "Besides," she added, "now thanks to Miyo, both Mr. Lincoln and I have found new friends."

CHECK FOR UNDERSTANDING

1. Why did Mrs. K.'s neighbor get angry about Mr. Lincoln?
2. How did Miyo's work for the class newspaper solve Mrs. K.'s problem?
3. Mrs. K. said both she and Mr. Lincoln had found new friends. Who did she mean?
4. Will Mr. Lincoln be as happy in his new home as he was with Mrs. K? Explain why you think he will or will not be.

Sequence of Events

If a friend asked you how Mrs. K.'s problem was solved in the story "The Rooster Who Understood Japanese," this is what you might say:

Miyo put an ad in the class newspaper.
Mr. Botts saw the ad.
Mr. Botts decided to take Mrs. K.'s rooster to his farm.
Mrs. K. had a new home for Mr. Lincoln.

The events are in the same story order. Think about time order as you read the next sentences.

Second, Mr. Botts saw the ad.
Finally, Mrs. K. had a new home for Mr. Lincoln.
First, Miyo put an ad in the class newspaper.
Then Mr. Botts decided to take Mrs. K.'s rooster to his farm.

What makes the second group of sentences different from the first? The second group is not in the same time order as in the story. But the clue words <u>first</u>, <u>second</u>, <u>then</u>, and <u>finally</u> help you understand what happens. These words help you order the events. The order that events happen is called the **sequence of events.**

Read the two groups of sentences below. How does each group tell about the sequence of events?

Peter told his teacher about a broken swing in the playground.
Mr. Pardo asked Miss Gold to fix the swing.
The swing was ready for play break.

Finally, the swing was ready for play break.
Next, Mr. Pardo asked Miss Gold to fix the swing.
First, Peter told his teacher about a broken swing in the playground.

The first group of sentences tells you the order, or sequence, of events. Can you understand the order of events in the second group of sentences? What words help you? Why are the words like first, next, and finally not needed in the first group of sentences? What would happen if a story began like this:

Peter got to school just in time.
Peter saw a bird nest on the street on his way to school.
He looked all over, but he couldn't find the birds.
He stopped to check the nest for eggs.

The sentences do not make sense in this order. What can you do to make the story clear?

Crowded places like cities have rules about pets. Rules keep pets from being a problem to other people. When Henry Huggins tries to take a dog home, he finds out about one of these rules.

What problem does Henry face when he tries to get his dog home? How does Henry finally solve the problem?

NO DOGS ALLOWED

by BEVERLY CLEARY

One Saturday Henry Huggins found a dog on the street. The dog had no collar, and he was so thin that his ribs showed. Henry had always wanted a dog, and this dog certainly needed a home. Henry decided to name the dog Ribsy. He called home to ask if he could keep him. His mother said he could, but he had to bring the dog home with him on the bus. Henry thought that would be easy. But there were a lot of things Henry didn't know about dogs and buses.

When the big green bus stopped at the
corner, Henry picked up his dog. Ribsy was
heavy. Henry had a hard time getting him on
the bus. Then the bus driver said, "Say,
Sonny, you can't take that dog on the bus."

"Why not?" asked Henry.

"It's a company rule. No dogs on buses."

"How am I going to get him home? I just
have to get him home."

"Sorry, Sonny, I didn't make the rule. No
animal can ride on a bus unless it's inside a
box or unless it's a guide dog."

"Well, thanks anyway," said Henry as he
lifted Ribsy off the bus.

"I guess we will have to get a box,"
Henry told his dog. "I'll get you on the
next bus somehow."

He went into the drugstore, followed closely by Ribsy. "Have you got a big box I could have, please?" he asked the man at the toothpaste counter. "I need one big enough for my dog."

The clerk leaned over the counter to look at Ribsy. "A cardboard box?" he asked.

"Yes, please," said Henry, wishing the man would hurry. He didn't want to be late getting home.

The clerk pulled the box out from under the counter. "This hair-tonic carton is the only one I have. I guess it's big enough, but why anyone would want to put a dog in a cardboard box I can't understand," he said.

The box was about two feet square and six inches deep. On one end was printed, "Don't Let Them Call You Baldy," and on the other, "Try Our Large Economy Size."

Henry thanked the clerk, carried the box out to the bus stop, and put it on the sidewalk. Ribsy padded after him. "Get in, fellow," Henry commanded. Ribsy understood. He stepped into the box and sat down just as the bus came around the corner.

As Henry lifted the box, Ribsy lovingly licked his face with his wet pink tongue.

The bus stopped at the curb. Henry stepped up into the bus. He asked the driver, "Will you please take the money out of my pocket? My hands are full."

The driver pushed his cap back on his head and exclaimed, "Full! I should say they *are* full! And just where do you think you're going with that animal?"

"Home," said Henry in a small voice.

"Not on this bus, you're not!" said the driver.

"But the man on the last bus said I could take the dog on the bus in a box," said Henry. "He said it was a company rule."

"He meant a big box tied shut. A box with holes punched in it for the dog to breathe through."

Just then Ribsy growled. "Shut up!" said Henry.

Ribsy began to scratch his left ear with his left hind foot. The box began to tear. Ribsy jumped out of the box and off the bus, and Henry jumped after him. The bus pulled away.

"Now see what you've done!" said Henry. "You've spoiled everything." The dog hung his head and tucked his tail between his legs. "If I can't get you home, how can I keep you?"

Henry sat down on the curb to think. It was so late and the clouds were so dark that he didn't want to waste time looking for a big box. His mother was probably beginning to worry about him.

People were stopping on the corner to wait for the next bus. Henry noticed a lady carrying a large paper shopping bag full of apples. The shopping bag gave him an idea. Jumping up, he snapped his fingers at Ribsy and ran back into the drugstore.

"You back again?" asked the clerk. "What do you want this time? String and paper to wrap your dog in?"

"No, sir," said Henry. "May I have one of those big shopping bags?"

Henry opened the bag and shoved Ribsy into it, hind feet first. Then he pushed his front feet in. A lot of Ribsy was left over at the top of the bag.

"I guess I'll have to have some string and paper, too," Henry said to the clerk.

The clerk handed a piece of string and a big sheet of paper across the counter.

Ribsy wiggled and whined, even though Henry tried to pet him through the paper. When the bus stopped, Henry climbed on. He dropped his money in the slot and squirmed through the crowd to a seat beside a big man near the back of the bus.

"Whew!" Henry sighed with relief. The driver was the same one he had met on the first bus! But Ribs was on the bus at last. Now, if Henry could only keep him quiet for fifteen minutes, they would be home and Ribsy would be his for keeps.

Ribsy was quiet for a while. Then he began to whimper and then howl. Crackle, crackle, crackle. Thump, thump, thump. Ribsy scratched his way out of the bag.

"Well!" exclaimed the big man, as he began to laugh. "If it isn't a skinny old dog in that bag!"

"He is not," said Henry. "He's a good dog."

Henry tried to keep Ribsy between his knees. The bus lurched around a corner and started to go uphill. Henry was thrown against the big man. The frightened dog wiggled away from him, squirmed between the passengers, and started for the front of the bus.

"Here, Ribsy, old boy! Come back here," called Henry and started after the dog.

"Catch that dog!" yelled the lady with the bag of apples.

Ribsy was scared. He tried to run and crashed into the lady's bag of apples. The bag tipped over and the apples began to roll toward the back of the bus, which was grinding up a steep hill. The apples rolled around the feet of people who were standing. Passengers began to slip and slide. They dropped their packages and grabbed one another.

Crash! A girl dropped an armload of books.

Rattle! Bang! Crash! A lady dropped a big paper bag. The bag broke open and pots and pans rolled out.

Thud! A man dropped a roll of garden hose. The hose unrolled and the passengers found it wound around their legs.

People were sitting on the floor. They were sitting on books and apples. They were even sitting on other people's laps. Some of them had their hats over their faces and their feet in the air.

Scree-e-ech! The driver threw on the brakes and turned around in his seat. Then he saw Henry making his way through the apples and books and pans and hose to catch Ribsy.

The driver pushed his cap back on his head. "OK, Sonny," he said to Henry. "Now you know why dogs aren't allowed on buses!"

"Yes, sir," said Henry in a small voice. "I didn't mean to make any trouble. My mother said I could keep the dog if I could bring him home on the bus."

The big man began to snicker. Then he chuckled. Then he laughed and then he roared. He laughed until tears streamed down his cheeks. All the other passengers were laughing too, even the man with the hose and the lady with the apples.

The driver didn't laugh. "Take that dog and get off the bus!" he ordered. Ribsy whimpered and tucked his tail between his legs.

The big man stopped laughing. "See here, driver," he said, "you can't put that boy and his dog off in the rain."

"Well, he can't stay on the bus," snapped the driver.

Henry didn't know what he was going to do. He guessed he would have to walk the rest of the way in the dark and the rain.

Just then a siren screamed. It grew louder and louder until it stopped right beside the bus.

A police officer appeared in the bus entrance. "Is there a boy called Henry Huggins on this bus?" he asked.

"I'm him," said Henry in a very small voice.

"Don't say 'I'm him,'" said the lady with the apples, who had been a schoolteacher. "You should say, 'I am he.'"

"You had better come along with us," said the police officer.

Henry and Ribsy followed the officer off the bus and into the squad car, where Henry and the dog sat in the back seat.

"Are you going to arrest me?" Henry asked timidly.

"Well, I don't know," said the officer. "Do you think you ought to be arrested?"

"No, sir," said Henry politely. He thought the police officer was joking, but he wasn't sure. It was hard to tell about grown-ups sometimes. "I didn't mean to do anything," said Henry. "I just had to get Ribsy home. My mother said I could keep him if I could bring him home on the bus."

"What do you think?" the police officer asked the other officer, who was driving the car.

"We-e-ell, I think we might let him off this time," answered the driver. "His parents must be worried about him if they called the police. I don't think they would want him to go to jail."

"Yes, he's late for his dinner already," said the other officer. "Let's see how fast we can get him home."

CHECK FOR UNDERSTANDING

1. What problem did Henry face when he tried to get his dog home?
2. How did Henry finally solve the problem of getting Ribsy on the bus?
3. When Ribsy got out of the bag on the bus, what did he do that caused people to slip and slide?
4. Why were the police officers looking for Henry?
5. Why would a guide dog, or a Seeing Eye dog, be allowed on a bus even though other dogs are not?

VERN

by GWENDOLYN BROOKS

When walking in a tiny rain
Across a vacant lot,
A pup's a good companion—
If a pup you've got.

And when you've had a scold,
And no one loves you very,
And you cannot be merry,
A pup will let you look at him,
And even let you hold
His little wiggly warmness—

And let you snuggle down beside.
Nor mock the tears you have to hide.

Using the Glossary

If you cannot understand the meaning of a word, or do not know how to say it, you usually go to a dictionary for help. The **dictionary** is a book that tells you a word's spelling, meaning, and pronunciation. **Pronunciation** is the correct way to say the word. Some books, such as this textbook, have their own small dictionary, called a glossary. A **glossary** lists special words found in the book itself.

Dictionaries and glossaries help you in many ways. They list words in **alphabetical order** to help you find them faster. To find a word that begins with the letter d, for example, look between words beginning with c and those beginning with e. Dictionaries and glossaries give the spelling of a word and how it can be divided. The word's **part of speech,** which might be noun, verb, adverb, or adjective, is listed after the word's pronunciation. Then the **meaning** or **meanings** of the word are given.

Here is an example of how the word lagoon might appear in a glossary. A word listed in a glossary or a dictionary is called an **entry word.**

> **la·goon** (lə gō̅n′) *n.* **1.** a shallow body of water partly or completely surrounded by a coral island or islands. **2.** a shallow body of sea water partly cut off from the sea by a narrow strip of land.

The first thing you see is the entry word itself spelled out. You see how the word is divided, and how each word part, or **syllable,** is pronounced. The word lagoon has two meanings in the example. You can tell that they are both nouns by looking at the letter n. after the pronunciation of lagoon.

A glossary needs a **pronunciation key** to explain the special way that the pronunciation of an entry word is given. You need to know how to pronounce a word in order to say it aloud, not just read it silently. Look closely at this pronunciation key.

PRONUNCIATION KEY
at; āpe; cär; end; mē; it; īce; hot; ōld; fôrk; wood; fo͞ol; oil; out; up; turn; sing; thin; this, hw in white; zh in treasure; ə stands for a in ago, e in taken, i in pencil, o in lemon, u in circus.

The pronunciation of lagoon is (lə go͞on′). You can see in the pronunciation key that the ə in the first syllable is pronounced like the a in the word about. The ə is called a **schwa.** Many words have the schwa sound, and the pronunciation key tells you the schwa sound for each vowel. The second syllable in lagoon has the same vowel sound /o͞o/, as the letters oo do in fool. Say lagoon aloud. The mark ′ after the second syllable is an **accent mark.** It tells you to stress, or say in a stronger way, the syllable the mark comes after. Some words have more than one accent. The word celebrate is pronounced sel′ ə brāt′. You stress the first syllable more than you stress the third. You can tell this by looking at the darker accent mark after the first syllable in celebrate.

Now read the following entry words taken from the glossary in your textbooks.

---

char·i·ot (char′ ē ət) *n*. a wagon with two wheels, pulled by horses.

dain·ty (dān′ tē) *adj*. fussy; picky.—**dain′ ti·ly,** *adv*.

lunge (lunj) *v*. **lunged.** to move suddenly toward.

mi·rac·u·lous (mi rak′ yə ləs) *adj*. hard to believe; amazing.

Look for all of the kinds of information you just learned about. How can you tell how to pronounce each word listed above? What does the n., v., adj., or adv. after a word tell you about it? Where is the meaning of each entry word given? You may see the letters n.pl. after a word in the glossary, as in this example.

cube (kyo͞ob) n.pl. **cubes.**

The letters <u>n.pl.</u> tell you that the plural form of the entry word is given next. The **plural** tells how to spell the word to mean more than one.

When you look for a word on a glossary page, you may find many other words beginning with the same letter. To locate the word you want quickly, you can use guide words. **Guide words** are the first word and the last word on a glossary or dictionary page.

Here is a list of entry words that might appear on a glossary page. What are the guide words for this page? Would you find the word <u>dinnertime</u> on this page?

dainty	**dinosaur**
deerstalker	**discourage**
destroy	**disturb**
diameter	**drought**

The guide words on this page are <u>dainty</u> and <u>drought</u>. You can tell that the word <u>dinnertime</u> would be on this page by looking at the guide words. All three words begin with the letter <u>d</u>. The second letter in <u>dinnertime</u> is <u>i</u>. The letter <u>i</u> comes between the <u>a</u> in <u>dainty</u> and the <u>r</u> in <u>drought</u>.

Using the glossary in this textbook, find the word <u>kimono</u>. What are the guide words on that page? What part of speech is <u>kimono</u>? How many syllables does it have? How do you know?

Pets are as different as people. Some are so quiet you barely know they're there. Others like to play and be with people all the time. Have you thought about which pet is right for you?

What does it take to have a happy, healthy pet?

WHO
WILL TAKE CARE OF ME?

by GIBBS DAVIS

PUPPY LOVE

More than any other pet, a puppy will need a lot of your time and direction. Remember, a puppy is a baby—a baby that has just been taken from its mother. Think how scared and sad you would feel.

Help your puppy get used to its new home. The first few days are the hardest.

Have a dog bed ready. Put a towel in the bottom. Cover the floor with newspapers. The newspapers will be your puppy's bathroom until it learns to go outside.

The hardest job is to teach your puppy to go to the bathroom outside. Take it on walks every few hours, and always after eating.

It takes time for puppies to learn. But don't get mad. Dogs learn faster with love.

Puppies need special puppy food to help them grow. Puppies eat three or four times a day. When older, they'll eat only once a day.

When your dog smells bad or its coat looks dirty, it's time for a bath. Most dogs don't like baths. That is why it takes two people to do the job. Be ready to get wet.

Brush your dog once a week. It's hard for a dog to sit still for this. Talk softly and pet your dog while brushing its coat. Ask someone older to cut your dog's nails.

Play time is important. Tug of war is fun for puppies. Use an old sock. Most dogs love to play catch the ball. It's good exercise, too.

"No" is an important word. Don't let your dog jump up on people. Say "Down." They should not bite people or get up on chairs. Teach with love. Let your dog know when it has done something well.

Take your dog to the veterinarian once a year. Your dog can't talk to you. Look for signs of your pet feeling sick. Has it lost interest in eating? Is it acting differently?

When your puppy is three to six months old, get it registered for a dog license.

KITTENS FOR SALE

It's always easy to find kittens. Just look in the newspaper. There are too many kittens without homes in the world.

While cats are not as loving as dogs, they are much easier to train and care for. Cats are very clever animals.

First, you must decide what kind of cat you want. One with long hair or short hair?

Make sure your kitten gets all the necessary shots. A veterinarian will help your pet stay healthy.

Kittens like to eat every few hours. As your kitten grows, it will need to be fed only once a day. Always keep a bowl filled with fresh water.

Once kittens are put in their cat box, they know just where to go to the bathroom. Cats learn fast. Clean out the cat box every day. Wash out the cat box once a week.

Cats are very clean animals. Your cat may never need a bath! But they do need to be brushed.

Get to know your cat. Learn when it wants to play and when it wants to be left alone to cat nap.

FISH FACTS

Before you buy your pet fish, here is some information you should know.

There are two kinds of fish—freshwater fish and saltwater fish. Decide which kind you want because they can't live together.

Fish that live in salt water are harder to care for. They get sick more often. But they come in every color in the rainbow.

Whatever fish you pick, make sure they are healthy. One sign of a sick fish are white spots. This condition is called "ick." Healthy fish swim freely and do not act tired.

Make sure your fish get along together. Some fish will fight and even eat other smaller fish.

You will need either a bowl or a fish tank. Make it look like home by adding rocks and plants. Make sure the water is warm enough.

Cleaning a fish tank is the hardest part of caring for fish. Clean it once a week. Using a hose, take out the dirty water. Then add fresh water. Wash the inside of the tank clean.

Feeding fish is easy. Lightly drop a tiny bit of dried food on the water every day. Be careful not to leave too much or your fish may get sick.

Keep sick fish away from healthy fish in a different "hospital" tank. Never touch a fish with dry hands. Wet them first or you'll hurt the fish's body.

You can spend hours fish watching. Slowly your fish will get used to you watching them. Don't tap on the glass tank until your fish get to know you better.

BIRD BITS

Would you like a pet that can be trained to sit on your finger? Or one that can sing? Then a bird is just right for you!

Before you choose a feathered friend, you should know a little bit about them.

Pet birds can't fly free. They must live in a cage. Place the cage in a warm spot. Birds get cold quickly. Cover the cage at night.

Give them fresh water and food every day. Pet stores sell special seeds for all birds.

Clean the cage once a week. You will also need to line the cage bottom with fresh paper every day.

Some birds like to take splash baths. Put a dish of water in the cage. Watch them have a bath party!

Canaries are known for their singing. But only a boy canary can sing. He will begin to sing at six months old. By one year old, he can sing a whole song!

Parakeets are fun pets. It takes time for them to get used to people. Once you are friends, your parakeet will eat from your hand. It will also happily sit on your arm, finger, or shoulder.

• •

CHECK FOR UNDERSTANDING

1. Why should you take your dog or cat to the veterinarian once a year?
2. What is the hardest part of caring for your fish?
3. What do you have to do to have a happy, healthy pet?

WRITE ABOUT *"Who Will Take Care of Me?"*

Sometimes people get a pet without thinking about what they need to do to care for it. Write four things you think people who want to own a pet should know about pet care before they get a pet.

Petey

by TOBI TOBIAS

Perhaps the biggest pet problem is something pet owners don't like to think about, the death of a pet. Most pets have shorter lives than people.

How does Emily know that something is wrong with Petey? Why is Emily not sure that she wants a new pet?

In the afternoon, like always, when I get home from school, I say hello to Mom. I check out what Benjy, my little brother, is up to and grab an apple. Then I run upstairs and drop my schoolbag on my bed and see what my silly old gerbil, Petey, is doing. Usually he's banging this juice can he's so crazy about against the glass sides of his cage. He makes a whole song of happy clinks and clunks. He does it at night, too. Daddy always says, when he comes in to kiss me, "How can you go to sleep with that racket?" But the real truth is I can hardly go to sleep without it. It's a friendly noise.

Or maybe he's building a fancy new nest for himself out of the cedar shavings and shredded burlap I put there for him. Or running himself dizzy in his exercise wheel. Or prying open a sunflower seed with his little paws and his tiny sharp teeth. Or washing his funny mouse face or grooming his funny mouse tail. When he hears me (he really knows the sound of my voice), he stops what he's doing. He sits up on his hind paws and looks around with his bright brown eyes. I put my hand into the cage, and he whisks right into it.

But this afternoon I get home late because it's my ice-skating day. It's beginning to get dark in my room, and I can hardly see him. But then I do. He's all huddled up in a corner of his cage like he's shivering, and when I call out, "Petey, I'm home. Want a piece of apple? Want a sunflower seed?" he doesn't sit up. Right away I know something bad is going to happen.

I call Daddy. He comes and looks, and I can tell by his face that what he's thinking is what I'm thinking, too.

"Pete's sick, Emily," he says. Then comes the worst part. Very slowly, Daddy says, "You know, honey, Petey's almost five years old now. That's getting to be pretty old for a gerbil—"

"No," I say. Just "No."

"OK, Em," Daddy says. "Let's see what we can do for him."

So we look in the *How to Care for Your Pets* book we have. It does not tell us any good news. You can't really doctor a gerbil, it says. You pretty much have to wait and see what happens. "If you have a sick gerbil one night," it says, "it's likely the next morning you'll either have a well gerbil or a dead gerbil." All I can say is the people who wrote that book must never have had a gerbil they loved or they wouldn't talk so smart.

Well, even if the book doesn't say anything you can do, we do everything we can think of. We change Petey's water, getting it just right between warm and cold, and we add a few drops of hamster medicine to it and try to coax Petey to drink. But he won't. Or maybe he can't. So we try plain water, because we think maybe he doesn't like the smell of the medicine. But Petey doesn't want that either. Then we shell some sunflower seeds and mash up the soft insides. I put the mash on my fingertip so Petey can lick it off. But he doesn't.

All the time we're doing this, Daddy is talking to me.

"Look at it this way, Em. Petey may be a well gerbil. The book says so. There's as much chance of that as—anything else."

"You were the one who said he was getting old," I yell, getting mad at him because I feel so terrible about Petey and not being able to do anything to help.

"Four or five years is a long life for a gerbil, Emmy. We've got to face up to that."

"It doesn't seem long to me," I say.

"Honey, think what a great time he's had with you. You've taken such good care of him. I don't just mean the feeding and keeping his cage clean. I mean all the talking and playing and loving."

Petey still won't take the food. There is a long silence among the three of us.

After a while Daddy says, "Em, if someone's going to die, it's better this way. It really is. Sometimes when animals or people get old, their sickness comes on slowly. It can be a very long time of hurting for them and everyone who loves them."

"Let's just be quiet," I say. "Maybe Petey's trying to sleep." But both of us know that Petey's never needed quiet for sleeping. Just the way I could sleep with his racket, he could sleep with mine.

After supper Daddy and I are watching over Petey again and Benjy comes in. "Here," he says, and he gives me a little piece off his blanket. "For Petey." I fold it up like a little pillow and put it under Petey's head. Benjy is scared. "Is Petey going to die?" he asks Daddy.

"I'm afraid he is, Ben," Daddy says, "but we're still hoping he won't."

When I wake up in the middle of that night, it's still the same with Petey. I try the food and the water again, but he doesn't care. Then I try just sitting by his cage and stroking his soft, shiny fur with my finger. Even if it doesn't help, maybe he knows I'm there. Anyway, I know I'm there, and that makes me feel a little better. After a while it gets cold sitting on the floor by Petey's cage, so I get back into my bed and pull up the covers the way Petey burrows into his nest of soft burlap and good-smelling shavings. I think about how cute he was when he was a little baby, and I guess I finally fall asleep.

In the morning, right when I wake up, I don't remember for a minute, but then I do. It hits me like someone threw a rock at my stomach. I go over to Petey's cage, very quietly. He's stretched out by his exercise wheel, not moving. I try to call Mommy and Daddy, but I haven't any voice left. I guess they know I need someone, though, and they come into my room. I forget which one of us says, "He's dead," but anyway I'm crying while Mommy holds me tight. I think she's crying a little, too.

Then, all of a sudden, we start to talk about all the things we remember about him, all his little ways and tricks, and how smart and beautiful he was. We're telling each other the crazy adventures he's had, like the time he knocked the screen lid off his cage and ran away. We chased after him, but that must have scared him. He wouldn't come out, and we couldn't find him anywhere. We finally found him on a shelf in the kitchen, curled up in a box of oatmeal, sleepy and full, with a funny look on his face like he was laughing.

Then we have breakfast.

I miss him. Every time I look at the empty cage I feel empty inside me. I miss him when Benjy finds a box of sunflower seeds and starts shelling them and eating the juicy insides. I miss him when Mommy scoops the frozen orange juice out of the can. I miss him when I see anything soft and shreddy that would be good to make a nest with. It's like things are all over the place, reminding me. Whenever I think about Petey, I love remembering all the good times we had, but then I feel awful because there won't be any more. Mostly I miss him when I'm going to sleep. It's so quiet.

It's starting to be spring now. I'm coming home from skating again, and Mommy's on the telephone. She says, "I'll ask her, Helen, and I'll let you know. Thanks a lot," and hangs up.

She says, "Hi," and, "Don't put those wet skates on the table," and gives me a kiss. I give her a wet apple kiss back. She says, "That was Helen," and she tells me that our friends Helen and George's two gerbils had a litter of five babies. Mommy says Helen and George know how bad I feel that Petey died. They'd like to give me two of the babies when they're old enough to leave their mother.

I test out the idea in my head, but it doesn't feel too good. No one, no one could be like Petey. I say, "Not right now."

Mommy says, "No, not right now. But in a while."

I say, "It won't be the same."

Mommy says, "I never said it would be the same. It can be different, Em, and still be good."

I'm going to think it over and let her know.

CHECK FOR UNDERSTANDING

1. How did Emily know that something was wrong with Petey?
2. What different feelings did Emily have while Petey was sick?
3. How did the others in Emily's family feel about Petey being sick?
4. Why was Emily not sure if she wanted a new pet after Petey died?
5. Do you think Emily will take the two gerbils the friends are offering? Explain why you think she will or won't.

THINK ABOUT IT

Think about the people and the pets in the stories you have read. What causes the problem, the pet or the people?

- What happened to Mog, and how did he get that way?
- What effect did Matthew's love of animals have on the Ladies' Literary League?
- Why did Mr. Lincoln, the rooster, have to find a new home?
- What made it difficult for Henry Huggins to get his new dog home?
- What are some of the things a pet owner must do in order to have a healthy, happy pet?
- What problem did Emily face that all pet owners have to face at some time?

After reading and thinking about these different pet problems, how do you think some of them might have been avoided?

WRITE ABOUT IT

Almost no pet animals live as long as people do. Do you think that is a good reason not to own a pet? Or do you think it is not a good reason for not owning a pet? Write your opinion in a paragraph. Give reasons for your opinion.

READ ABOUT IT

The Faithless Lollybird by Joan Aiken. Doubleday Publishing Co., 1978. Half of the stories in this collection tell about animals and their problems.

*A Home Is to Share—and Share—and Share—*by Judie Angell. Bradbury Press, 1984. Two children take stray animals into their home one at a time. Suddenly their business booms when the town's animal shelter closes.

Mishmash and the Big Fat Problem by Kelly Cone. Houghton Mifflin Co., 1982. Mishmash, the dog, has a problem. He's been overeating because his friend Pete has had no time to do things with him. Then, Pete involves his dog and himself in an exercise program.

Tumble, Tumble, Tumbleweed by Pat Lowery Collins. Albert Whitman, 1982. John adopts a tumbleweed one summer when it blows into his yard. When "Pet Day" is announced in school, John has a problem because his "pet" has been slowly disappearing. His family comes up with an interesting solution.

2

TOGETHER IS BETTER

Can you imagine what your life would be like if you never saw or spoke to other people? It wouldn't even be very human. That's because people don't live very well without other people. Even so, it isn't always easy to be part of a friendship or even a family.

As you read the stories in this unit, think about the people you meet. Think about the ones who think they want to be alone. Ask yourself how they find out, one way or another, that "together is better."

NIGHT RUMBLES

by PATRICIA MacLACHLAN

Emma is worried about the "night rumbles" in her bedroom. She decides she will be happier sleeping somewhere else.

What are the "night rumbles"? Why does Zachary keep telling Emma about bugs and grubs and wild wolves?

"I am not going to sleep in my bedroom tonight," announced Emma.

"Why not?" asked Zachary. "Because of the mess?"

"No," said Emma. "Because of night rumbles."

"What are night rumbles?" asked Zachary.

"I am not sure," said Emma, "but my friend Noah has them. He says they only come at night. He says they will come here soon. They are furry things with legs who live in the closet, and whiskery shadows in the corners of the room, and a long arm that lives under the bed and tries to grab you when you jump into bed."

"Have you seen them yet?" asked Zachary.

Emma shook her head. "Not yet. And I am not going to."

"Where will you sleep?" asked Zachary.

"In the backyard," said Emma. "In the tent."

"In the tent!" exclaimed Zachary. He loved sleeping in the tent. "But what about bugs and grubs and wild wolves?"

"I am not afraid of bugs and grubs," said Emma, "and Wayne will protect me from wild wolves. In the tent there are not a lot of corners with boxes and closets and chairs and toy chests for things to hide in. Or in back of. Or under."

"No mess," said Zachary, nodding.

"No mess," agreed Emma. She began to pack her things.

Uncle Elliot poked his head in the door. "Where are you going?"

"Emma is not going to sleep in her room tonight," said Zachary. "Because of night rumbles. The furry things with legs who live in the closet, and the whiskery shadows in the corners of the room, and the long arm that lives under the bed and tries to grab you when you jump into bed."

"Where?" asked Uncle Elliot, peering cautiously around the room.

"They only come at night," said Emma. "When the lights are off."

"You could leave the lights on," suggested Uncle Elliot.

Emma shook her head. "Then I'd see them," she said. She looked at Uncle Elliott. "My parents say there are no such things as night rumbles."

"And I am sure they are right," said Uncle Elliot heartily. He opened the closet door. "No furry things here," he said.

90

"They're hiding behind the shoe boxes," said Emma.

Uncle Elliot looked in each corner of Emma's room.

"There are no whiskery shadows," he said.

"They're waiting for you to leave," said Emma.

Uncle Elliot got down and peered under the bed.

"No arm," he announced.

"There will be," said Emma. "I am going to sleep outside in the tent."

"The tent! All by yourself?" exclaimed Uncle Elliot. "Won't you be scared? I was always scared."

91

"I could sleep out there with you," said Zachary eagerly.

"No," said Emma. "By myself. I'll have Wayne. And my battery lamp and my pencils and pens and writing paper and some books and a bag of nuts and Eleanor, my cactus."

"Just remember bugs and grubs and wild wolves," whispered Zachary.

They went to the garage to look for the tent. Aunt Evelyn was doing her ballet exercises with her hand on the car door handle.

"We're putting up the tent, Ev," said Uncle Elliot. "Emma's going to sleep outside tonight because of the night rumbles."

Aunt Evelyn looked at Emma. She raised her eyebrows.

Emma sighed. "The furry things with legs who live in the closet," she explained again, "and the whiskery shadows in the corners of the room, and the long arm that lives under the bed. My mother and father and Uncle Elliot do not think there are such things."

"Great loving George!" exclaimed Aunt Evelyn. "Of course there are! I slept in my closet for two weeks because of the *Whispers*."

"The *Whispers?*" Emma moved closer to Zachary.

"The *Whispers* rustled and murmured all night long in my room when I was your age," said Aunt Evelyn. "But won't you be lonely out in the tent by yourself? I would be real lonely."

"No," said Emma. "I'll have Wayne."

"I'd be lonely," said Aunt Evelyn.

Zachary and Uncle Elliot carried the tent out to the backyard.

"Can we put it up on the little hill?" asked Emma.

Zachary shook his head. "Everything will fall out the front door of the tent. You will, too."

93

"How about under the tree?" suggested Emma.

"The acorns will fall on the tent roof," said Zachary.

"That will not be good," said Emma. "Wayne barks at dropping acorns."

Finally they decided on a flat place in the middle of the yard where it would be easy for Wayne to watch for wild wolves.

Zachary helped Uncle Elliot put up the tent. He helped when Uncle Elliot tried to put up the tent upside down. He helped pound in the tent stakes when Uncle Elliot put them in the wrong place. He straightened the ropes so that the tent would not lean to one side. He helped by getting a bandage and ice when Uncle Elliot hit his finger with a hammer.

"It's done," called Uncle Elliot, collapsing on the ground and crawling inside the tent to pant in the shade.

Later, Emma moved all her things to the tent. Zachary did not help. She moved her sleeping bag first, and her Martha Mouse pillow. She moved her lamp and her pencils and pens and paper and books and the bag of nuts and Eleanor, her cactus. Then Emma waited for nighttime. She ate dinner early so that she could get into the tent before the night rumbles came to her room. Zachary took a twenty-seven minute shower and left soggy towels and cold puddles on the floor. Emma took a bubblebath and lost a herd of plastic animals and three marbles under the suds. Then it was nighttime.

"Good night, Emma," said Uncle Elliot. "Are you sure you won't be scared?"

"No," said Emma. "I won't be scared."

"Will you be lonely?" asked Aunt Evelyn.

"No."

"Don't you want me to come, too?" asked Zachary.

"No," said Emma. "Come, Wayne."

"Remember bugs and grubs and wild wolves," called Zachary as Emma padded out to the tent.

It was quiet and peaceful in the tent, and Wayne fell asleep right away, snorting and wheezing a bit. Emma read a chapter of her book, ate some nuts, then watched the stars outside the tent flap. She closed her eyes.

"Emma." She woke up with a start as Zachary climbed inside the tent, dragging his sleeping bag. "Were you asleep already?"

"Yes," said Emma.

"I'm sorry I scared you about bugs and grubs and wild wolves," said Zachary. "I wanted to sleep in the tent with you."

"That's all right," said Emma. "You can stay for a while."

Emma moved over, and together they rolled Wayne farther into the corner.

"Good night, Emma."

"Good night, Zach."

It was quiet and peaceful again, and Zachary fell asleep right away.

"Emma?" Just as Emma was about to fall asleep, she saw Aunt Evelyn crouched down with a thermos bottle in her hand. "I thought you must be lonely. And thirsty. I brought you some hot chocolate."

Emma smiled. "Zach's here. Come in."

Aunt Evelyn crawled inside the tent. She lay down next to Emma. She yawned. "Now you won't be lonely," she said.

97

Emma drank some hot chocolate and watched Aunt Evelyn fall asleep. She wiggled back inside her sleeping bag, gently moving Wayne's head with her foot, and waited for Uncle Elliot.

"*Psst*. Emma."

"Yes, Uncle Elliot."

"Are you scared? Hey, everyone's here." He crawled over Zachary and pushed Wayne around. "Got any nuts left?"

Together they watched the stars while Uncle Elliot ate nuts. He lay down next to Zachary. "Boy," he said just before he fell asleep, "this isn't scary at all, is it?"

Emma turned over carefully and counted the stars. She thought about the bugs and grubs sleeping deep underneath the tent. She watched awhile for wild wolves. But she didn't worry. There was no room for wild wolves in the tent. Emma smiled and closed her eyes. No room for the *Whispers*, whoever they were. And no room at all for night rumbles.

CHECK FOR UNDERSTANDING

1. What were the "night rumbles"?
2. Why did Zachary keep telling Emma about bugs and grubs and wild wolves?
3. Why do you think Emma insisted on sleeping in the tent alone?
4. Why do you think Emma ended up having so much company in her tent that night?

WRITE ABOUT *"Night Rumbles"*

Emma took some of her favorite things into the tent with her. Along with her sleeping bag and a lamp, she took things like a favorite pillow, her cactus, a snack, and her dog.

Write a paragraph telling what you would take with you if you were sleeping in a tent.

IN THE PITCH OF THE NIGHT

by LEE BENNETT HOPKINS

In the pitch of the night,
where there isn't a light,
comes a very bad rabbit
with a horrible habit
of filling my head
with dangers—

> wanting to take me
> through forests
> where strangers
> and ghoulies
> high in the trees
> try to leap out at me.

So I say,
"Listen here, rabbit.
I'm sick of your habit.
I've had enough
of your nightmarish fright.

My bed is *my* bed
Not some rabbit-filled head

    of monsters and dragons
    and weird plants that bite!

Now get out of my room!
Go on your own way!
Sleep has to come
before
    night
      turns
        to
          day!"

Consonant Digraphs

Say the word <u>hu</u>ngry. You hear both <u>n</u> and hard <u>g</u>. Now say <u>thing</u>. You do not hear the sound <u>n</u> or the hard <u>g</u> sound. You hear a new sound, /ng/. It is the sound that makes <u>thing</u> a different word than <u>thin</u>. The two letters <u>n</u> and <u>g</u> together make a sound that is different from the sound that <u>n</u> alone or <u>g</u> alone makes. It is heard in the words <u>ring</u>, <u>sang</u>, <u>long</u>. Two letters that together make one sound are called a **digraph.**

Now say the word <u>chair</u>. What two consonant letters does <u>chair</u> begin with? They are <u>c</u> and <u>h</u>. These two letters together make the sound that is heard at the beginning of the word <u>chair</u>. That sound is different from the sound that <u>c</u> alone or <u>h</u> alone makes. Both letters make the sound /ch/.

Read this list of words. Each word begins with a **consonant digraph**—consonant letters that together make one sound.

chair	what	shop	this
chop	white	ship	thank
chain	wheel	shut	thing
chip	whale	shoe	that

- What do you see that is the same about the words <u>chair</u>, <u>chop</u>, <u>chain</u>, and <u>chip</u>?
- Which words in the list begin with the first two consonant letters in <u>show</u>?
- What do you see that is the same about the words <u>this</u>, <u>thank</u>, <u>thing</u>, and <u>that</u>?
- Which words begin with the first two consonant letters in <u>when</u>?

Sometimes two consonant letters stand for one sound at the end of a word. Say the word <u>both</u>. It ends with two consonant letters, <u>t</u> and <u>h</u>. These letters stand for the sound heard at the end of <u>both</u>. That sound is different from the sound that <u>t</u> alone or <u>h</u> alone makes.

You may even see three consonant letters that make one sound at the end of a word, such as <u>pitch</u>. Say <u>pitch</u>. Listen to the sound in the word. The three consonant letters <u>tch</u> stand for one sound /ch/.

Here is a list of words that end with two or three consonant letters that make one sound.

both	wash	wrong	beach	pitch
mouth	push	string	which	catch
teeth	fish	hung	march	ditch
bath	crash	rang	such	match

CHIN CHIANG
and the
DRAGON'S DANCE

by IAN WALLACE

Emma's aunt and uncle thought that being
together was better so that Emma would be
safe and not afraid. But Chin Chiang must do
a new dance in front of many, many people.
He is not sure he wants to be together with
anyone right now.

How does Chin Chiang feel about being in
the dragon's dance? Why is the dance so
important to people?

From the time Chin Chiang stood only as
high as his grandfather's knees, he had
dreamed of dancing the dragon's dance. Now
the first day of the Year of the Dragon had
arrived and his dream was to come true.
Tonight he would dance with his grandfather.
But instead of being excited, Chin Chiang
was so scared he wanted to melt into his
shoes. He knew he could never dance well
enough to make Grandfather proud of him.

He stopped sweeping the floor of his family's shop and looked into the street. There his mother and father were busy with other shopkeepers, hanging up paper lanterns shaped like animals, fish, and birds.

"It's time to practice our parts in the dragon's dance for the last time before the other dancers arrive, Chin Chiang. The afternoon is almost over," called Grandfather Wu from the bakeroom behind the shop.

"If I were a rabbit, I could run far away
from here," Chin Chiang said to himself.
"But then Mama, Papa, and Grandfather
really would be ashamed of me." So very
slowly he walked into the bakeroom where
Grandfather Wu stood waiting. He was
wearing the splendid fierce dragon's head that
he would put on again that night for the
parade.

"Pick up the silk tail on the floor behind
me," said his grandfather from inside the
dragon's head. "Together we will be the most
magnificent dragon that anyone has ever
seen."

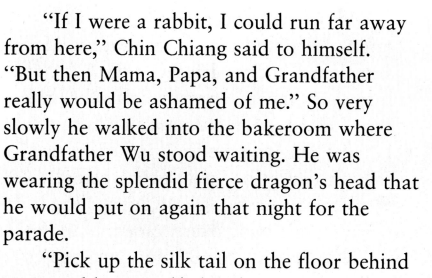

Chin Chiang did as he was asked, but as his grandfather started to dance, Chin Chiang did not move. "Grandfather can hide under the dragon's head," he whispered, "but if I trip or fall, I have nowhere to hide. Everyone will say, 'There goes clumsy Chin Chiang.'"

Grandfather Wu stopped dancing. "A dragon must have a tail as well as a head," he said gently.

Chin Chiang looked down at his shoes. "I can't dance the dragon's dance," he said.

"You have trained for a long time, Chin Chiang. Tonight, when you dance, you will bring tears of pride to your parents' eyes. Now come, join me and practice just as we have practiced before."

But when Chin Chiang tried to leap, he tripped, stumbled, and fell. Why had he ever thought he could dance the dragon's dance? Why had he ever wanted to? He was much too clumsy.

He jumped up and ran—away from his grandfather, out of the shop, into the market street. He stopped long enough to pick up a rabbit lantern, poke two holes for eyes, and shove it over his head.

"Look, look. It's the dragon's tail!" called Mrs. Lau, dangling a speckled salmon for Chin Chiang to see. "Tonight, when you dance, the Great Dragon who lives in the clouds above the mountains will be honored. Next year he will fill our nets with beautiful fish like this."

Chin Chiang turned away.

"And he will grow oranges of a size and color never seen before," called Mr. Koo.

"What they say is true," added Mr. Sing. "The Great Dragon will bring good fortune, if your dance pleases him."

But Chin Chiang remembered what one of the other dancers had once told him. If the dance was clumsy, the Great Dragon would be angry. Then he might toss the fruit from the trees and flood the valley. *It will all be my fault,* thought Chin Chiang. *Grandfather Wu will have to choose someone else to dance with him.* He waited to hear no more and raced across the market street.

"Our fish!" called Mrs. Lau.

"Our oranges!" called Mr. Koo.

Chin Chiang turned the corner.

"Our dance," called Grandfather Wu, from the doorway.

Looking through the lantern, Chin Chiang hurried along the road by the sea to the public library, which he had visited many times when he wanted to be alone. He opened the door and ran upstairs, round and round, higher and higher, up, up, up, to the door at the top that led out to the roof.

From his perch in the sky, he could see the mountains rising above the sea and below him the animal lanterns, which would glow like tiny stars tonight. Chin Chiang felt happier than he had for many days.

"I never expected to meet a rabbit on top of this roof," called a strange voice.

Chin Chiang turned around quickly. A woman carrying a mop and pail was coming toward him.

"I'm not a rabbit," he said shyly. "I am Chin Chiang," and he pulled off the lantern.

"Oh, that's much better," she said. "Greetings, Chin Chiang. My name is Pu Yee. May I enjoy the view with you?" She didn't wait for a reply. "In a little while I'll be watching the New Year's parade from here. I used to dance the dragon's dance when I was young, but not anymore. My feet are too old."

"My grandfather dances the dragon's dance," said Chin Chiang, "and his feet are as old as yours."

Pu Yee laughed. "His old shoes may move his old bones, but my feet will never dance again."

A wonderful idea suddenly came to Chin Chiang. What if he had found someone to dance in his place? He would show Pu Yee his part in the dance right now. No one would see them if they tripped or fell. "You can help me practice what my grandfather taught me," he said.

"Oh, my creaky bones, what a funny sight that will be," said Pu Yee.

"You can dance," he told her. Cautiously Chin Chiang gave a little jump. Pu Yee jumped, too. He shook slowly at first and she shook, too. Next they leaped into the air, landed together, and spun on their heels. Before long Pu Yee had forgotten her creaky bones. Then Chin Chiang stumbled and fell.

"Let's try again," said Pu Yee, picking him up.

While they danced, darkness had crept down slowly from the mountains to the city below. Then, from far off, Chin Chiang heard the lilting tune of pigeons with whistles tied to their tail feathers. They had been set free from their cages in the marketplace and were flying high above the buildings. Chin Chiang knew this meant that the New Year Festival had begun.

"We must go, Pu Yee. We're late," said Chin Chiang. "The pigeons are flying free."

"*I'm* not late," she replied. "I'm staying here."

But Chin Chiang pulled her by the hand, and they hurried down the stairs together—round and round, down, down, down, to the market street. The sound of firecrackers exploded in their ears while the eager crowd buzzed and hummed. Chin Chiang pushed his way forward, but Pu Yee pulled back. In the noise and confusion, Chin Chiang let go of her hand, and suddenly he came face to face with the dragon whose head was wreathed in smoke.

"Where have you been, Chin Chiang? I have been sick with worry," called Grandfather Wu in a muffled voice. Chin Chiang did not reply. "Come now, take up the tail before the smoke is gone and everyone can see us."

Chin Chiang stood still, his feet frozen to the ground. The clamor of the street grew louder, stinging his ears. "I can't dance, Grandfather," he said.

Grandfather Wu turned away. "You can dance, Chin Chiang. Follow me."

"Look, look. Here comes the dragon!" called Mr. Sing. The crowd sent up a cheer that bounced off the windows and doors and jumped into the sky.

Chin Chiang was trapped. Slowly he stooped and picked up the tail. Grandfather Wu shook the dragon's head fiercely until Chin Chiang started to kick up his heels to the beat of the thundering drum.

114

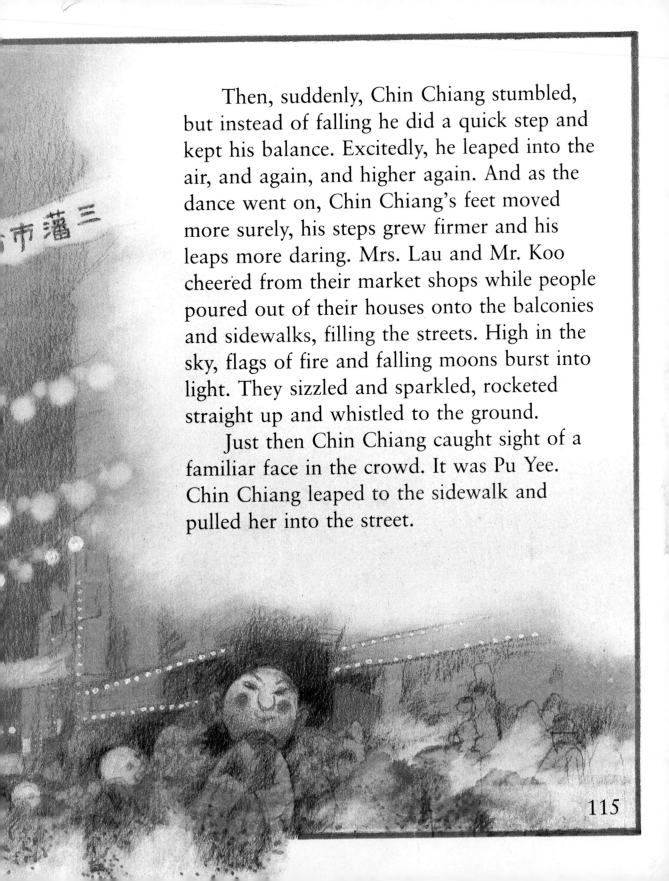

Then, suddenly, Chin Chiang stumbled, but instead of falling he did a quick step and kept his balance. Excitedly, he leaped into the air, and again, and higher again. And as the dance went on, Chin Chiang's feet moved more surely, his steps grew firmer and his leaps more daring. Mrs. Lau and Mr. Koo cheered from their market shops while people poured out of their houses onto the balconies and sidewalks, filling the streets. High in the sky, flags of fire and falling moons burst into light. They sizzled and sparkled, rocketed straight up and whistled to the ground.

Just then Chin Chiang caught sight of a familiar face in the crowd. It was Pu Yee. Chin Chiang leaped to the sidewalk and pulled her into the street.

115

恭賀新禧　一家平安

"I can't, Chin Chiang," she said, pulling away. "My bones. My feet. My knees."

"Pu Yee, yes, you can," Chin Chiang said to her. "Look at me!" Hesitantly she took hold of the tail and together they kicked up their heels just as they had on the rooftop, while throngs of people cheered them on. Up one street and down another they danced, to the beat of the thundering drum.

All too soon the dragon lifted its head and shook its tail for the last time. The dance was over. Pu Yee hugged Chin Chiang close.

Grandfather Wu smiled inside the dragon's head. "Bring your new friend to our home for dinner, Chin Chiang," he said. Pu Yee and Chin Chiang hopped quickly over the doorstep and into the bakeshop.

116

The family exchanged gifts of teas in wooden boxes, new clothes, and small red envelopes of Lucky Money. Then they sat together to share plates of meat dumplings and fish, bowls of steaming soup, and trays of wonderful pastries and cakes and fresh fruit.

"To Chin Chiang, the very best dragon's tail I have ever seen," said Grandfather Wu, raising his glass.

Chin Chiang's face glowed with pride. "To a prosperous Year of the Dragon," he said, raising his glass to his mama, papa, grandfather, and his new friend, Pu Yee.

CHECK FOR UNDERSTANDING

1. At the beginning of the story, how did Chin Chiang feel about being in the dragon's dance? Why?
2. Why was the dragon's dance so important to people?
3. How did Chin Chiang plan to solve the problem of dancing in the parade?
4. What happened during the dance before Chin Chiang began to enjoy his part?
5. If Chin Chiang has a chance to dance in another parade, how do you think he will feel about it? Explain your answer.

SNOWHOUSES

by MINNIK as told to FRED BRUEMMER

Some places in the world are harder to live in than others. The land may not offer much food. The weather may be very cold. In places like these, people often depend on each other for help. The Arctic, where the Inuit people live, is such a place. Look for ways the Inuit people help each other in the story.

What is the weather like in the Arctic? What are three main steps in building a snowhouse?

If you travel as close to the North Pole as you can go on land, you will come to the part of the world my people call "the beautiful land." We are the Inuit (in'ū it'). You may know us by the name that the North American Indians gave us: Eskimos.

For thousands of years my people have lived in the Arctic. Today there are about 110,000 of us in Siberia, Alaska, Canada, and Greenland. Outsiders say no other people live in a climate as harsh as ours. They say our winters are long, cold, and dark. They are right about that. Our winter lasts nine months or longer. Ice covers our lakes and much of the Arctic Ocean. Snow buries the land. The average January temperature is −25°F (−32°C). We also have about two months of darkness.

But like my ancestors, I love "the beautiful land." And like my ancestors, I enjoy the hunt. So three days ago, my friend Ekalun and I left our village to hunt caribou. This afternoon Ekalun and I were lucky. We killed a caribou. We are grateful to the animal for giving us food. The meat of the caribou is delicious. I will give the skin of the caribou to my mother. She has promised to make me a hooded jacket of caribou skin like the one my grandfather used to wear. Today almost everyone wears jackets made in factories, but I don't want to forget our old ways.

After the hunt, Ekalun and I built an igloovigaq (ig lōō′vuh gak), or snowhouse. You may call this an igloo. But to us, an igloo is a house made of any material, not just snow. Our grandfathers lived in snowhouses all winter long. We don't. Like the rest of the Inuit, we live year round in houses made of wood. But an igloovigaq is very handy on a hunting trip. It will keep us safe and warm.

Now I am tired. I think I will join Ekalun inside the snowhouse and go to sleep. To see how Ekalun and I made it, read on.

A Hunter's Igloo

Building a snowhouse is much easier when there are two people to share the work. I begin cutting large blocks of snow with my handsaw. Ekalun lays these blocks in a circle. Then he adds more blocks of snow, trimming each one so that it tilts inward. The walls lean more and more inward until they become a roof. At last Ekalun reaches up and pops in the key block, the last block of snow.

To make the snowhouse windproof, I stuff snow into the cracks between the large blocks. In only one

hour, Ekalun and I have built a shelter that will keep us warmer than a tent.

After we finish the snowhouse, Ekalun and I bring our gear inside. We unpack and cook our evening meal on a camping stove. The light from our lantern makes our igloo-vigaq glow in the dark.

Inside a Family Igloo

When I was a little boy, my family and I lived in a

snowhouse all winter. So did all of the other families in our village in northern Canada. (The Inuit of other areas built winter houses of sod, stone, or wood.)

The inside walls of the house were often lined with sealskins. The temperature in the house could get up to 70°F (21°C) before the walls would begin to melt. It usually felt so warm that people took off many of their clothes soon after they came inside.

The times have changed, but I am glad I remember many of the old ways. I have told my children stories of the past. And I hope they will pass the tales of the old days on to their children and grandchildren.

1. My father made knives from bone and ivory. He used this snow knife to make each snow block tilt inward when he was building this house.

2. The only time a dog was allowed in the snowhouse was when it had puppies.

3. My mother's hood made a great place for me to play and sleep.

4. Everyone sat and slept on a bed made of snow. It was covered with warm animal skins.

5. During the long winters, my mother made clothing, blankets, and tents from caribou skins.

6. The clothes dryer worked well. You just spread your wet clothes on a rack. Then you lit a lamp below it.

7. The winter snowhouse had an entrance made of snow blocks. It sloped downhill so that warm air (which always rises) would not escape from the house.

8. One corner of the snowhouse was a smelly, food storage area. There were piles of frozen seals in it.

9. These sled dogs were left outside so they wouldn't gobble up the food inside the igloo.

CHECK FOR UNDERSTANDING

1. By what other name are the Inuit known?
2. What is the weather like in the arctic?
3. What does the word *igloo* mean to the Inuit?
4. What are three main steps in building a snowhouse?
5. What did the inside of a typical snowhouse look like?

Make a Mini I·G·L·O·O

Idea by KIMBERLY KERIN

When the wind roars and the temperature drops way below freezing, traveling across the Arctic could mean big trouble. But not for the Inuit, or Eskimos. They just take out their handsaws and knives and build a house, or igloo, of hard-packed snow.

You may not be in the Arctic. But you can build a mini igloovigaq that looks a lot like the ones the Inuit build.

You'll need: white frosting in a tube and a box of sugar cubes (rectangular or square) or about 3 dozen marshmallows cut in half. You may want to try other materials, too.

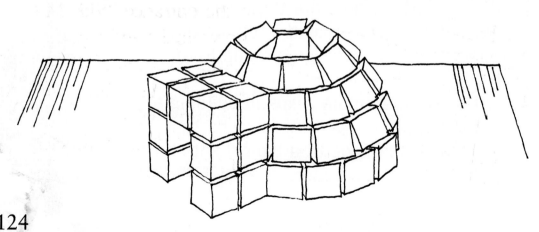

What to do: On a white piece of paper, make a ring of frosting about 5 inches (13 cm) in diameter. Place your first "snow block" anywhere on the ring. Put some frosting on one side of another block. Then push it against the first block (see drawing 1). Keep adding snow blocks around the circle in the same way until the first layer is complete.

Put a thick coat of frosting on top of the first layer of blocks. Place a snow

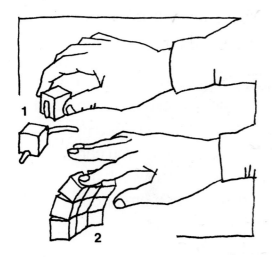

block on this frosting. Gently push down on the inside edge of the block. Most of the frosting will ooze to the outside. The block will tilt toward the center of the circle (see drawing 2). Keep building inward and upward until there is only a small hole in the roof of your igloo. (This hole allows smoke from a cooking fire to escape).

To get into an igloo-vigaq, the Inuit may cut a hole through two of the snow blocks. Sometimes they build a tunnel leading to the entrance. With 14 snow blocks and some frosting you can make a tunnel, too (see drawing of finished igloo).

Now sit back and enjoy your mini igloo!

Main Idea

You know that a paragraph or longer piece of writing is made up of sentences. One of these sentences tells what the paragraph or piece of writing is about in a more general way than the other sentences. This sentence states the **main idea.** The thought that it expresses holds together all of the other thoughts in the paragraph. Look for the one thought that holds the other sentences together as you read the paragraph below. It is from "Snowhouses."

> Outsiders say no other people live in a climate as harsh as ours. They say our winters are long, cold, and dark. They are right about that. Our winter lasts nine months or longer. Ice covers our lakes and much of the Arctic Ocean. Snow buries the land. The average January temperature is $-25°F$ ($-32°C$). We also have about two months of darkness.

Which one thought tells what the paragraph is about in a general, not exact, way? It is the thought expressed in the first sentence. This sentence tells the main idea of the paragraph, how harsh the Arctic climate is. You can see that the other sentences tell exact ways in which the climate is harsh. These sentences explain more about the main idea sentence.

The main idea sentence comes at the beginning of a paragraph in many cases. But it is not always given at the beginning of a paragraph. To find the **main idea sentence,** look for the sentence that tells in a general way what the paragraph is about. This general idea is called the **topic.** In the paragraph on page 126, the topic was the harsh Arctic climate. Find the topic of this paragraph from "Snowhouses."

> I will give the skin of the caribou to my mother. She has promised to make me a hooded jacket of caribou skin like the one my grandfather used to wear. Today almost everyone wears jackets made in factories, but I don't want to forget our old ways.

The topic is how the writer tries to keep old Inuit ways alive. Which sentence best states this in a general way? It is the last sentence, the main idea, that explains why. So, when you do not spot the main idea right away, read carefully and identify the topic of the paragraph.

Find the most general statement in the paragraph below. Does this main idea sentence come at the beginning or the end of the paragraph?

> Food is one link with their past for many people. Folk songs also help keep the past alive. Some people even wear a special style of clothing. People have many ways of remembering how their relatives lived long ago.

I Need a Friend

by SHERRY KAFKA

All by myself
I can dig for treasure
But I need a friend
to hold the map.

All by myself
I can grow a flower
But I need a friend
to give it to.

All by myself
I can throw a ball
But I need a friend
to catch it.

All by myself
I can tell a joke
But I need a friend
to laugh.

All by myself
I can climb a tree
But I need a friend
to give me a boost.

All by myself
I can draw a picture
But I need a friend
to look at it.

All by myself
I can eat a sandwich
But I need a friend
to have a picnic.

All by myself
I can run
But I need a friend
to race.

All by myself
I can skin my knee
But I need a friend
to feel sorry.

All by myself
I can know a secret
But I need a friend
to whisper it to.

All by myself
I can guess a riddle
But I need a friend
to tell it.

All by myself
I can dream a story
But I need a friend
to listen to it.

All by myself
I can play alone
But I need a friend
for sharing.

Best friends don't do everything together, but they do many things together. What is it like to suddenly lose a close friend? The girl in the story finds out when her friend begins to spend more time with someone else.

What is something the girl telling the story likes to do that her friend Robin doesn't like? How did Robin's finding a new friend end up helping the storyteller?

Losing Your Best Friend

by CORINNE BERGSTROM

Having a best friend is like having a brother or a sister. No, it's even better. Best friends are special in their own way. Having a best friend and losing her can be very sad. Sometimes it's even a little scary, like going somewhere by yourself for the first time.

I know because I had a best friend. Her name was Robin. We did everything together. We rode bikes. We jumped rope. We skateboarded in summer and ice-skated in winter.

We shared secrets. We even liked the same clothes. We did everything together except pretend. Robin thought it was silly to pretend, but I thought it was fun. I learned a lot when I pretended.

Sometimes I pretended that I was a guide in a national park. I told people all about the trees and animals. I learned lots of things about nature just by studying my own backyard.

Sometimes I pretended to be a librarian. I told stories and showed pictures to little boys and girls. I helped them find books. I even checked out some of my own storybooks for them to read.

I imagined what it might be like to be in an airplane or to fly through space. I'd fly between stars to the moon, and around and around from planet to planet.

So many times, I wished Robin would pretend with me. We had a lot of fun doing other things, but it would have been nice if we could have pretended together, too.

Then something strange began to happen to Robin and me. Something I didn't like at all.

New neighbors moved in up the street. Sandy and Benny were twins. Sandy was in Robin's and my class at school. Benny was in the other third grade class. I asked why they weren't in the same room. Sandy said it was because schools don't want twins to be together all the time.

After school, Robin invited our new neighbors to ice-skate with us. Benny couldn't come, but Sandy did. We thought we were good skaters, but Sandy made my eyes open wide. She leaped and spun like a star.

Afterward, we went for hot chocolate. Robin and Sandy decided to start a club. Sandy would be president and Robin would be vice president. They said I could be secretary.

Robin usually stopped for me on the way to school. The next morning she didn't come. I asked her why. She said she stopped for Sandy instead, so they could make plans for the club.

I reminded her that I was secretary. She said it was their job to make the plans. Then I could write them down.

It didn't feel good to be left out. I felt tears coming, but I was angry, too. I didn't know if I should cry or holler.

The next day, I watched for her, but Robin didn't stop again. She and Sandy went by. Benny was walking behind them throwing snowballs at their backs. Maybe they couldn't stop. Or maybe they hadn't even thought about me.

At school, Miss Wilkerson asked for two volunteers to stay indoors for recess and help her with some chores. Usually she picked Robin and me. She knew we would work hard. This time, though, she picked Robin and Sandy instead.

I asked if I might help, too. But she said she only needed two people. I know it wasn't Robin's fault, but I gave her a dirty look as I went out to the playground. I began to feel I didn't have a best friend anymore. Everything was Robin and Sandy . . . Robin and Sandy.

Some girls in our class were playing snow statues. I wished that I could play, too. But I was afraid to join them. Was I shy? I had never thought about it before. Robin and I had been best friends for a long time.

Then I saw Sandy's brother, Benny. He was watching some boys playing tag. Would he have liked to play with them? Was he shy, too? I wanted to talk to him. But I remembered the snowballs.

Finally, recess was over. Robin said they had finished plans for the club while they were helping Miss Wilkerson. They would tell them to me after school. I felt a little better.

The first club project was a trip to the museum. Sandy's mother took us there. Robin and Sandy didn't want Benny to come, but I didn't mind. If our club had lots of people, Sandy might find a new friend. Then Robin and I could be best friends again.

At the museum, Robin and Sandy pointed at all the exhibits and laughed. There were lots of things to look at. I saw drawings of animals, statues of Indians, pictures of cave dwellers all dressed in fur, and even bones of a dinosaur.

Robin giggled and laughed, but I didn't. I pretended I was living in the days of the dinosaurs. Fear gripped me at the thought of live monsters.

Then I dreamed I was queen of the jungle. Birds called me through the trees, and crocodiles moved slowly around me. Natives bowed before me and sang songs.

I glanced at Benny. His eyes had a faraway look. Was it possible that he was dreaming, too?

Robin and Sandy grabbed my arms. They wanted me to see some valuable rocks. I was glad they wanted me with them. But I missed dreaming. They would only have laughed if I had shared my thoughts.

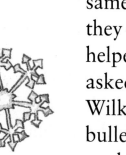

Days passed slowly. Our club stayed the same . . . Robin and Sandy . . . except when they wanted me to do something. When they helped Miss Wilkerson at recess, no one asked me to play. One day when Miss Wilkerson asked me to help her change the bulletin board, she asked Jerry, too. All he could talk about was his new 10-speed bike. But that was better than being alone.

Then it happened.

I finally convinced Robin and Sandy that we should have others in our club. I asked Benny to be our first new member. He was glad to join. I was glad, too. Before long, we had eight people in our club. Maybe now Sandy would find another friend, and Robin and I would be best friends again.

Our club decided to have a winter carnival. We divided up into groups to plan the different things the carnival would have. Here was my chance to be with Robin! But Robin wanted to work with Sandy, planning the refreshment stand.

I didn't care what I did after that. I didn't even care if I was part of the carnival at all. Then Benny suggested we do a play.

A play! I liked that. Acting was like pretending. Another girl, Pam, wanted to work with us. I wished Robin wanted to pretend just once. She might have liked it if she tried. But she didn't. And Sandy was just like her.

Our play was about a snow queen. I was really excited. I got to be the snow queen. My mother made my costume. She used an old bride's dress she found at a garage sale. It was beautiful. Pam was the snow princess. Her costume was made from ruffled curtains. We had a lot of fun practicing in them.

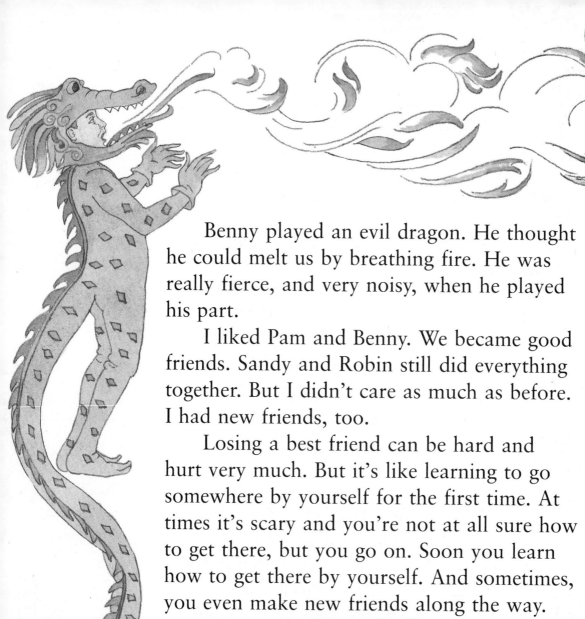

Benny played an evil dragon. He thought he could melt us by breathing fire. He was really fierce, and very noisy, when he played his part.

I liked Pam and Benny. We became good friends. Sandy and Robin still did everything together. But I didn't care as much as before. I had new friends, too.

Losing a best friend can be hard and hurt very much. But it's like learning to go somewhere by yourself for the first time. At times it's scary and you're not at all sure how to get there, but you go on. Soon you learn how to get there by yourself. And sometimes, you even make new friends along the way.

Our play was a big success. Now Benny, Pam, and I are planning a puppet show. We'll write the story, and make and work the puppets, too. And the biggest surprise of all— Sandy and Robin asked to help. That's OK with me. I can't wait to begin.

CHECK FOR UNDERSTANDING

1. What were some of the things that the girl telling the story and Robin shared as best friends?

2. What was something the girl liked to do that her friend Robin didn't like?

3. What happened to change the friendship of the girl and Robin?

4. What two feelings did the girl have when Robin explained why she didn't stop for her on the way to school the first time?

5. How did Robin's finding a new friend end up helping the girl telling the story?

WRITE ABOUT *"Losing Your Best Friend"*

Robin and Sandy liked to do things together. Benny, Pam, and the girl telling the story found that they liked doing things together. Write a paragraph that explains how the children in each of the two groups are alike. Tell whether you think the two groups will do very many things together or not.

141

My Friend Jacob

by LUCILLE CLIFTON

Friends may sometimes be very different from each other. In "My Friend Jacob," Sam and Jacob are different in many ways, but they like each other and they also help each other.

Why does Sam's mother warn him about getting hurt by Jacob? What do you think makes it difficult for Jacob to do things that are easy for other seventeen-year-olds?

My best friend lives next door. His name is Jacob. He is my very, very best friend.

We do things together, Jacob and I. We love to play basketball together. Jacob always makes a basket on the first try.

142

He helps me to learn how to hold the ball so that I can make baskets, too.

My mother used to say, "Be careful with Jacob and that ball. He might hurt you." But now she doesn't. She knows that Jacob wouldn't hurt anybody, especially his very, very best friend.

I love to sit on the steps and watch the cars go by with Jacob. He knows the name of every kind of car. Even if he only sees it for just a minute, Jacob can tell you the kind of car.

He is helping me be able to tell cars, too. When I make a mistake, Jacob never ever laughs. He just says, "No no, Sam, try again."

And I do. He is my best best friend.

When I have to go to the store, Jacob goes with me to help me. His mother used to say, "You don't have to have Jacob tagging along with you like that, Sammy." But now she doesn't. Jacob helps me to carry, and I help Jacob to remember.

"Red is for stop," I say if Jacob forgets. "Green is for go."

"Thank you, Sam," Jacob always says.

Jacob's birthday and my birthday are two days apart. Sometimes we celebrate together.

Last year he made me a surprise. He had been having a secret for weeks and weeks, and my mother knew, and his mother knew, but they wouldn't tell me.

Jacob would stay in the house in the afternoon for half an hour every day and not say anything to me when he came out. He would just smile and smile.

On my birthday, my mother made a cake for me with eight candles, and Jacob's mother made a cake for him with seventeen candles. We sat on the porch and sang and blew out our candles. Jacob blew out all of his in one breath because he's bigger.

Then my mother smiled, and Jacob's
mother smiled and said, "Give it to him, Jacob
dear." My friend Jacob smiled and handed me
a card.

HAPPY BIRTHDAY SAM
JACOB

He had printed it all himself! All by
himself, my name and everything! It was neat!

My very best friend Jacob does so much
helping me, I wanted to help him, too. One
day I decided to teach him how to knock.

Jacob will just walk into somebody's
house if he knows them. If he doesn't know
them, he will stand by the door until someone
notices him and lets him in.

145

"I wish Jacob would knock on the door," I heard my mother say.

So I decided to help him learn. Every day I would tell Jacob, but he would always forget. He would just open the door and walk right in.

My mother said probably it was too hard for him and I shouldn't worry about it. But I felt bad because Jacob always helped me so much, and I wanted to be able to help him.

I kept telling him, and he kept forgetting. So one day I just said, "Never mind, Jacob, maybe it is too hard."

"What's the matter, Sam?" Jacob asked me.

"Never mind, Jacob," was all I said.

Next day, at dinnertime, we were sitting in our dining room when I and my mother and my father heard this real loud knocking at the door. Then the door popped open and Jacob stuck his head in.

"I'm knocking, Sam!" he yelled.

Boy, I jumped right up from the table and went grinning and hugged Jacob, and he grinned and hugged me, too. He is my very, very, very best friend in the whole wide world!

CHECK FOR UNDERSTANDING

1. What things did Jacob and Sam enjoy doing together?
2. Why did Sam's mother warn him about getting hurt by Jacob?
3. Why was Sam so pleased with Jacob's birthday card?
4. How did Sam's mother's feeling about Jacob change from the beginning to the end of the story?
5. What do you think makes it difficult for Jacob to do things that are easy for other seventeen-year-olds?

Elements of a Story

Stories are a lot like checkers or other board games you have played. To play a board game, you need the board and the pieces you move around the board. You also need to know how the game is played. You need to know the object of the game. You need to know what must happen in order for someone to win the game. Stories have similar things. To tell a story, an author needs a setting, characters, and a plot.

Setting

The setting of a story is like the board on which a game is played. The **setting** is the time and the place in which a story happens. The setting is important to the story. A game of checkers cannot be played on a board meant for another game. In the same way, a story about a girl who wants to sleep in a tent in the backyard cannot take place in a big city where there are no backyards. Just as you need the right board to play a game, stories need the right setting.

Characters

Have you ever wanted to play a game and discovered you had lost some of the pieces? You cannot play a board game without the pieces. You need the pieces to make the moves that make the game happen. In the same way, an author cannot tell a story without characters. The **characters** do the things that make the story happen.

The characters in a story are usually people, but they don't have to be. Story characters can be animals or robots or even trees or flowers. Even if the characters are not people, they usually behave like people and have the thoughts and feelings people have.

Plot

When you play a board game, there is a beginning, a middle, and an end. At the beginning, you choose the pieces you want to play with, and you put the pieces in the starting position. In the middle of the game, you move the playing pieces around. Making the moves involved in playing the game leads to someone winning the game. When someone wins, it is the end of the game.

The **plot** is all the events that happen in a story. Like a game, a plot has a beginning, a middle, and an end. At the beginning of the story, you meet the characters and learn about the setting. In the middle of the story, you learn what happens to the characters. You learn about the events that move the story from the beginning to the end. You learn about problems the characters face, and you see what they do to solve them. At the end of the story, the characters solve their problems and the story is over—just like the board game is over when somebody wins.

LUCKY CHARMS
AND
BIRTHDAY WISHES

by Christine McDonnell

The first day of school brings children together in new and different groupings. Emily finds herself with Leo and Ivy. Since they are silly and she is shy, Emily isn't sure what will happen. But new seats might mean new friends. . . .

What does Emily look for on her way to school the first day? Why is Emily afraid her good-luck charm has turned into a bad-luck charm?

NEW SEAT, NEW FRIENDS

Emily Mott walked to school slowly on the first day of the new term. It was warm and sunny, too early for the leaves to turn. If it weren't for school, this would have been a good day for swimming. It was still warm enough for shorts, but Emily was wearing a dress. Her mother had asked her to.

"It's nice to dress up a little on the first day of school," Mrs. Mott said. "It celebrates a new beginning."

Emily didn't mind. The dress was sort of a long T-shirt anyway. It didn't itch and it wasn't fussy.

As she walked to school, Emily searched the ground for a lucky charm. A rock with a ring around it, or a very big acorn with a top that could come off like a hat. Maybe a penny. Something she could put in her pencil case and think of as a good-luck charm. It was just a game, but when the familiar brick school came into sight before she had found a charm, she felt a twinge of disappointment.

Her new classroom was on the second floor, with windows overlooking the playground. Mrs. Higgenbottom, her new teacher, sat at her desk giving out name tags.

"Your name, dear?" she asked, giving Emily a warm smile.

"Emily Mott."

Mrs. Higgenbottom handed her a name tag shaped like a ship. "We'll all be explorers together this year," she said.

After each ship had been pinned onto a dress or a shirt, Mrs. H. gave out the seats. "These are just to start with. We might change in a few weeks."

Emily's desk was the middle desk in the cluster by the window. Ivy Adams sat on one side, and Leo Nolan on the other.

Emily smiled at Ivy, one of those halfway sorts of smiles, the kind you could pretend wasn't really a smile if the other person didn't smile back. But she didn't have to worry. Ivy Adams grinned back right away. Leo Nolan smiled when he looked up from the details he was adding to his name tag. He had drawn a cannon on the deck and a pirate symbol on the flag of his ship.

Emily leaned back in her chair and looked around. This was a good seat. It was near the paperback book rack in case she wanted something to read during class. It was right next to the window. She could see the maple tree across the street, and a large patch of sky.

She wasn't sure about Ivy and Leo, though. She didn't know them very well. Last year she had sat across from them both. Leo used to get into trouble, she remembered. And Ivy was best friends with Phyllis. Emily decided to wait and see. Maybe they would all become friends. Maybe not. You never could tell.

By the end of the first week in school, Emily liked her seat so much she hoped Mrs. Higgenbottom would forget about changing. Ivy and Leo were friendly and silly.

In other grades Emily had always been very well-behaved in school. She was smart and liked to learn new things. Also, she was a little bit shy, and this made her quiet. A serious child, the teachers used to call her. But you couldn't be serious sitting between Ivy and Leo.

"Hey, Emily, what did the apple say to the grape?" Leo asked.

"I don't know."

"You're very appealing. Get it? A-peeling. Like an apple peel and peel me a grape." Leo was chuckling so hard at his own joke that little tears of laughter spilled out of the corners of his eyes, and he wiped them off with the back of his hand.

Emily smiled, more at his laughter than at the joke. Ivy laughed. Then all three of them got the giggles together, and that made Leo laugh harder than ever.

Mrs. Higgenbottom gave them a cold look, and they tried to settle down. But it's hard to stop when you've got the giggles. From time to time one of them would let out a snort or a chuckle, and that would start them off again.

Mrs. Higgenbottom gave them another cold look, longer this time. They finally quieted down and went back to doing their arithmetic sheets. . . .

On her way to school the next week, Emily found the lucky charm she had been looking for. It was a smooth, flat, oval rock, smoke-gray, with a thin white stripe circling it. It was exactly the right size; it fit in the center of her palm. She tucked it in her pocket, and when she got to class, she put it in her pencil case.

Ivy saw her.

"What's that?"

"A rock I found on my way to school."

"Why're you putting it in there?"

Emily hesitated. She didn't want Ivy to think she was silly. But everybody knew that rocks with stripes around them are lucky.

"It's a lucky charm. It has the stripe around it."

She handed it to Ivy.

"Is it really lucky?" Ivy asked.

Emily nodded. "Every stone with a stripe that goes completely around it is lucky. My father told me."

Ivy examined the rock, running her fingers over its cool surface and tracing the white band.

"Do you think I could find one?"

"Sure, if you look carefully."

Ivy looked all week but couldn't find one. Leo was looking for one, too. By Friday they were both discouraged.

"Guess we just aren't lucky," said Leo.

Emily tried to cheer them up. "You don't really need a stone to be lucky."

"Well, it sure might help," said Ivy.

All day Friday Emily worried. Maybe Leo and Ivy won't like me because of this, she thought. I wish I had never found the lucky stone. Maybe it's a bad-luck charm, not a good-luck charm.

That afternoon the class had a spelling test. Ivy and Leo each missed one word. Emily got every one right.

"See," said Ivy. "It does help to have a lucky charm."

Leo nodded.

Emily didn't really think that the stone had anything to do with getting one hundred on the test. She had always been a good speller. But she didn't want to argue about it. She just wanted to be friends.

On Saturday Emily went to visit her Grandmother Eve. After lunch they went for a walk on the beach near her grandmother's house. The sun made the sand glint, and the wind made whitecaps on the waves. They walked quietly together, Grandma looking for sea glass and shells, Emily searching for lucky stones.

"Gran, are stones lucky if you don't find them yourself?" Emily asked.

Grandma thought about it for a minute. Emily could tell she was thinking because she made a tiny wrinkle between her eyebrows, and she pushed her hands deep into the pockets of her corduroy pants.

"I think a lucky stone can bring you luck if the person who gives it to you is your friend and truly wants you to be lucky."

Emily listened carefully, then kept on searching for stones with rings around them. Near the jetty she found a little white one with a band of black, and just below the steps that led to her grandmother's house, she found a speckled stone with a white stripe around it. She placed both of them carefully in her pocket.

On Monday Emily gave the little white stone to Ivy and the speckled one to Leo. They were surprised and pleased.

"Hey, thanks!" said Ivy. "I really wanted this."

"Me, too," said Leo. "Now we're like a team. We should call ourselves the Lucky Stones."

Emily is happy to have Leo and Ivy as new friends. They joke and have fun together. Now that they all three have lucky stones, maybe they can have lucky adventures! You can find out what kinds of things they do by reading the book Lucky Charms and Birthday Wishes *by Christine McDonnell.*

CHECK FOR UNDERSTANDING

1. What did Emily look for on her way to school the first day?
2. What did Emily like about her seat at school?
3. Why was Emily afraid her good-luck charm had turned into a bad-luck charm?
4. What did Emily's grandmother tell her about "lucky stones"?
5. Why did Emily feel it was going to be a good year?

WRITE ABOUT *"New Seat, New Friends"*

Sometimes friends are good for each other *because* they are different. Write a paragraph telling how you think Emily's friendship will be good for Leo and Ivy. Write another paragraph telling how Leo and Ivy's friendship will be good for Emily.

161

THINK ABOUT IT

Think about the characters in the stories you have read. What made each of them want to be alone? What made them decide that they didn't want to be alone after all?

• Why didn't the other people in the story pay attention to Emma's wish to be alone?

• What were two ways in which Chin Chiang learned that "together is better"?

• What are some of the ways the Inuit people help each other?

• How did the girl telling the story think that she and Robin could be best friends again?

• What makes Sam and Jacob's friendship special?

• How did Emily change after she made friends with Leo and Ivy?

After reading and thinking about these different kinds of friendships, who in the unit would make a good friend for you?

WRITE ABOUT IT

If friends followed rules of friendship, what do you think the five most important rules would be? Write your five rules in a paragraph.

READ ABOUT IT

I Don't Live Here! by Pam Conrad. E. P. Dutton & Co., Inc., 1984. Nicki's new house is too big, too old, and too far away from her friend Lisa. As she secretly dreams of going back, she meets up with Jeffrey. They watch the building of a big spider web. Her plans change!

The Kid Next Door and Other Headaches by Janice Lee Smith. Harper & Row, Publishers Inc., 1984. Two neighbor boys, who share lots of things, disagree at times about neatness, pets, and how to treat girl cousins.

New Life, New Room by June Jordan. Thomas Y. Crowell, 1975. Three children suddenly have to move into one bedroom. Their father lets them work out all on their own how they will share the space.

Ramona Forever by Beverly Cleary. William Morrow & Co., Inc., 1984. Ramona Quimby is worried because her father is having trouble finding a new teaching job. She is afraid they may have to move away from her friends.

A NEW
OUTLOOK

Sometimes people get stuck
with the way things are. They
get so stuck they can't think of
a way to get unstuck. They
may even want more than
anything to do things a
different way. But, somehow,
they just can't see a new way.
It's at times like these that
people need a new outlook,
even if it comes from a cat
named Bangs or a moose that's
blue.

As you read this unit, ask
yourself who has gotten stuck,
and how they are stuck. Think
about what new outlook you
might give the person. See if
the new outlook you think of is
the same one in the story.

Like every cook, Mr. Breton wants to know if people like his food or not. But no one ever says much about it. Then out of the woods comes a big, hungry blue moose, bringing with it a new outlook.

How are the blue moose's manners different from those of the people from the town? How does Mr. Breton feel at the end of the story?

MOOSE MEETING

by MANUS PINKWATER

Mr. Breton had a little restaurant on the edge of the big woods. There was nothing north of Mr. Breton's house except nothing, with trees in between. When winter came, the north wind blew through the trees. It froze everything solid. Then it would snow. Mr. Breton didn't like it.

Mr. Breton was a very good cook. Every day, people from the town came to his restaurant. They ate gallons of his special clam chowder. They ate plates of his special beef stew. They ate fish stew and Mr. Breton's special homemade bread. The people from the town never talked much. They never said anything about his cooking.

"Did you like your clam chowder?" Mr. Breton would ask.

"Yup," the people from the town would say.

Mr. Breton wished they would say, "Delicious!" or "Good chowder, Breton!" All they ever said was, "Yup." In winter they came on skis and snowshoes.

Every morning Mr. Breton went out behind his house to get firewood. He wore three sweaters, a scarf, galoshes, a woolen hat, a big checkered coat, and mittens. He still felt cold. Sometimes animals came out of the woods to watch Mr. Breton. Raccoons and rabbits came. The cold didn't bother them. It bothered Mr. Breton even more when they watched him.

One morning there was a moose in Mr. Breton's yard. It was a blue moose. When Mr. Breton went out his back door, the moose was there, looking at him. After a while, Mr. Breton went back in, closed the door, and made a pot of coffee while he waited for the moose to go away. It didn't go away. It just stood in Mr. Breton's yard, looking at his back door. Mr. Breton drank a cup of coffee. The moose stood in the yard. Mr. Breton opened the door again. "Shoo! Go away!" he said.

"Do you mind if I come in and get warm?" the moose said. "I'm just about frozen." The moose brushed past him and walked into the kitchen. His antlers almost touched the ceiling.

The moose sat down on the floor next to Mr. Breton's stove. He closed his eyes and sat leaning toward the stove for a long time. Mr. Breton stood in the kitchen, looking at the moose. The moose didn't move. Wisps of steam began to rise from his blue fur. After a long time the moose sighed. It sounded like a foghorn.

"Can I get you a cup of coffee?" Mr. Breton asked the moose. "Or some clam chowder?"

"Clam chowder," said the moose.

Mr. Breton filled a bowl with creamy clam chowder and set it on the floor. The moose dipped his big nose into the bowl and snuffled up the chowder. He made a sort of slurping, whistling noise.

"Sir," the moose said, "this is wonderful clam chowder."

Mr. Breton blushed a very deep red. "Do you really mean that?"

"Sir," the moose said, "I have eaten some very good chowder in my time. Yours is the very best."

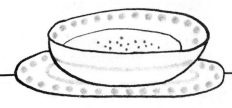

170

"Oh my," said Mr. Breton, blushing even redder. "Oh my. Would you like some more?"

"Yes, with crackers," said the moose.

The moose ate seventeen bowls of chowder with crackers. Then he had twelve pieces of hot gingerbread and forty-eight cups of coffee. While the moose slurped and whistled, Mr. Breton sat in a chair. Every now and then he said to himself, "Oh my. The best he's ever eaten. Oh my."

Later, when some people from the town came to Mr. Breton's house, the moose met them at the door. "How many in your party, please?" the moose asked. "I have a table for you. Please follow me."

The people from the town were surprised to see the moose. They felt like running away. But they were too surprised. The moose led them to a table. He brought them menus, looked at each person, snorted, and clumped into the kitchen.

"There are some people outside. I'll take care of them," he told Mr. Breton.

The people were whispering to one another about the moose, when he clumped back to the table.

"Are you ready to order?"

"Yup," the people from the town said. They waited for the moose to ask them if they would like some chowder, the way Mr. Breton always did. But the moose just stared at them as though they were very foolish. The people felt uncomfortable. "We'll have the clam chowder."

"Chaudière de Clam. Very good," the moose said. "Do you desire crackers or homemade bread?"

"We will have crackers," said the people from the town.

"I suggest you have the bread. It is hot," said the moose.

"We will have bread," said the people from the town.

"And for dessert," said the moose, "will you have fresh gingerbread or Apple Jacquette?"

"What do you recommend?" asked the people from the town.

"After the Chaudière de Clam, the gingerbread is best."

"Thank you," said the people from the town.

"It is my pleasure to serve you," said the moose. The moose brought bowls of chowder balanced on his antlers.

At the end of the meal, the moose clumped to the table. "Has everything been to your satisfaction?" he asked.

"Yup," said the people from the town, their mouths full of gingerbread.

"I beg your pardon?" said the moose. "What did you say?"

"It was very good," said the people from the town. "It was the best we've ever eaten."

"I will tell the chef," said the moose.

The moose clumped into the kitchen. He told Mr. Breton that the people from the town had said that the food was the best they had ever eaten. Mr. Breton rushed out of the kitchen and out of the house. The people from the town were sitting on the porch, putting on their snowshoes.

"Did you tell the moose that my clam chowder was the best you've ever eaten?" Mr. Breton asked.

"Yup," said the people from the town, "we said that. We think that you are the best cook in the world. We have always thought so."

"Always?" asked Mr. Breton.

"Of course," the people from the town said. "Why do you think we walk seven miles on snowshoes just to eat here?"

The people from the town walked away on their snowshoes. Mr. Breton sat on the edge of the porch and thought it over. When the moose came out to see why Mr. Breton was sitting outside without his coat on, Mr. Breton said, "Do you know those people think I am the best cook in the whole world?"

"Of course they do," the moose said. "Do you want me to go into town to get some crackers? We seem to have run out."

"Yes," said Mr. Breton. "And get some asparagus, too. I'm going to cook something special tomorrow."

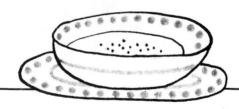

"By the way," said the moose, "aren't you cold out here?"

"No, I'm not the least bit cold," Mr. Breton said. "This is turning out to be a very mild winter."

CHECK FOR UNDERSTANDING

1. Where was Mr. Breton's restaurant?
2. What did Mr. Breton keep asking the people from the town, and what was their answer?
3. How were the blue moose's manners different from those of the people who came from town to eat?
4. When he waited on the people from town, what were three things the moose did differently from the way Mr. Breton did them?
5. How did Mr. Breton seem to feel at the end of the story?

WRITE ABOUT *"Moose Meeting"*

Without being asked, the moose began to do certain jobs for Mr. Breton. Describe the work the moose did, and tell why you think he did it.

The Sounds /oo/, /o͞o/, /ou/, /oi/

Read these words.

wood   room   out   voice

These words have the vowel sounds /oo/, /o͞o/, /ou/, and /oi/.

You hear the vowel sound /**oo**/ in the words <u>wood</u>, <u>could</u>, and <u>put</u>. What do you notice about the spelling of the sound in these words? It is spelled differently in each word. It is spelled with <u>oo</u> in <u>wood</u>, <u>ou</u> in <u>could</u>, and <u>u</u> in <u>put</u>.

Here are some words with /oo/.

look	put	should	cook
book	could	pull	full

The vowel sound /o͞o/ is heard in the words <u>do</u>, <u>room</u>, and <u>blew</u>. In these words, /o͞o/ is spelled in three different ways. It is spelled with <u>o</u> in <u>do</u>, with <u>oo</u> in <u>room</u>, and with <u>ew</u> in <u>blew</u>.

Here are some words with /o͞o/.

balloon	knew	two
grew	soon	few
to	boot	afternoon

The vowel sound /**ou**/ is heard in <u>ou</u>t. The sound /ou/ is spelled <u>ou</u> in the words <u>cloud</u>, <u>sound</u>, and <u>mouth</u>, but it is spelled <u>ow</u> in <u>how</u> and <u>crown</u>.

Here are some words with /ou/.

shout	down	cow	found
town	out	proud	now

You hear the vowel sound /**oi**/ in the word <u>voice</u>. The sound /oi/ can also be spelled two ways. It can be spelled <u>oi</u>, as in <u>noise</u> or <u>spoil</u>. It can also be spelled <u>oy</u>, at the end of a word.

Here are some words with /oi/.

toy	join	boil	oil
coil	soil	boy	enjoy

Look for words with the sounds /oo/, /$\overline{oo}$/, /ou/, or /oi/ as you read these sentences.

This food tastes good!
Let's enjoy it together now.

THE GRIZZLY BEAR
WITH THE
GOLDEN EARS

by JEAN CRAIGHEAD GEORGE

Golden Ears is a bear who finds she can
get what she needs for herself and her cub by
scaring other bears—and people. But when
she gets scared herself, her outlook changes.
In what way does Golden Ears become a
problem for the park ranger? What do you
think happened to make her cub disappear?

The people of the North called her Golden Ears. She had round blond ears that set her apart from all other bears. She was a brown grizzly bear of Alaska. The great bear the Eskimos worshipped because it walks like a human.

Golden Ears lived in the cold forest of Katmai*. In the summer she and the other bears of the forest fished for salmon in the Brooks River. In the fall they wandered the mountains eating blueberries and cranberries. In the winter when ice storms crackled, they slept under the roots of the spruce trees in the foothills of the rugged Aleutian Mountains.

Golden Ears was three years old.

One sunny noon in June she brought her little golden-eared cub to meet the bears of the Brooks River. They were gathered on the riverbank.

The bears stepped back and lowered their heads. A mother bear with a cub is both queen and king. It is the most adored bear of all bears. Even Ursus stepped back. Ursus was the one-thousand-pound male grizzly who had killed a little cub, as some male bears do when they find one alone and unguarded.

*Katmai (Kat′mī)

179

Below Brooks Falls the red salmon gathered by the thousands to leap up the waterfall. The fish leave the Pacific Ocean. They swim up the rivers to the same streamlets where they were born. There in the water under the starflowers and blue gentians, they lay their eggs and die. As they swim home, they are eaten by wolves, eagles, and gulls. Along the Brooks River they are eaten by the people at fish camp, the ranger, and the rollicking, diving, wonderful brown grizzly bears.

Golden Ears splashed into the water. She snapped at a fish and missed. Golden Ears swatted another fish and missed.

In a pool nearby, Kasvik, her friend, put her head under the water. She saw a salmon, snapped her jaws and caught it. She carried it up on the shore. Golden Ears wanted that fish. She was boss bear. So she lunged at Kasvik, bluffing her, as bears do. Kasvik dropped the salmon and ran. Golden Ears sat down by her golden-eared cub. She cleaned the bones from the fish and daintily ate it.

The next day she bluffed Kuka and took his fish. The following day she pounced at her sister and took her fish. Feeling very sure of herself, she walked up to Ursus. "Yarl," she growled. The enormous grizzly dropped his fish and backed away.

Golden Ears did not bother to fish. She just bluffed all the bears on the Brooks River and ate until she was full. Then she romped with her cub in the aspen grove and watched the eaglets in their nest.

One summer afternoon when the sun flashed on the river, Golden Ears came upon a fisher who was pulling a huge fish out of a pool. She hesitated. She was afraid of people. But she was boss bear. She charged the fisher. He dropped his pole and lunch and ran in terror back to fish camp. He reported the terrible bear with the golden ears.

Out in the river, Golden Ears tore open the lunch bag. She found candy bars, sandwiches, and cake. She carried them back to the aspen grove, and she and her cub ate them.

Ursus stalked the forest behind them.

When the winds of August blew and the eaglets took their first flight over the Brooks River, the salmon run slowed down. The bears of the Brooks River caught fewer and fewer fish. A young boy came to the waterfall and cast his line. He caught a big salmon and hauled it ashore.

Golden Ears rushed at the boy and growled. He dropped his pole, fish, and lunch and ran full speed to the ranger. "A bear with golden ears almost ate me," he said. "So I dropped my fish and lunch, and ran."

"That is the last time *that* bear will bluff," said Karen the ranger. "I am going to give her a sleeping drug."

She called the forester. "Come in your helicopter and get Golden Ears," she said. "Put her and her cub in the net. Carry them hundreds of miles away, then let them go."

Karen picked up a dart filled with a sleeping drug. She put it in the bear gun. She asked the boy to lead her to Golden Ears.

Golden Ears was eating sandwiches and candy in the aspen grove. Ursus was nearby. Presently he lumbered past them and dove into the river. He belly flopped on a salmon, and Golden Ears got to her feet. She challenged Ursus. He ran up the bank. The fish was hers. When she had cleaned and eaten the fish she climbed back to her cub.

He was gone.

The odor of the male grizzly Ursus mingled with the scent of her little cub. She looked for him in the aspen grove. She searched the meadow. She ran through the flowers. She called and roared in anguish.

She thundered into the forest out of sight of the ranger, knocking down trees, uprooting ferns and moss as she hunted for her cub. Then she stood up. Walking on two feet, she sniffed and called. No little cub answered.

All night Golden Ears searched the riverbank. She woofed and cried. Just before the misty morning dawned, she lowered her head. The once proud Golden Ears shuffled miserably toward her den on the mountain.

The bears of the Brooks River stood still and listened. "Woof," Golden Ears called. (Where are you, little one?)

"Woof."

"Woof."

A gray wolf howled. The eaglets called. Golden Ears gave up the hunt. She walked in silence.

"Wuf," came a small voice.

A tree swayed. Golden Ears snapped up her head, rose to her hind feet and stared. In the top of the spruce her golden-eared cub looked down at her.

Golden Ears whimpered and woofed as her cub backed into her arms. She flopped back on her haunches and hugged him. She licked, kissed and loved him.

Then she got to her feet. Her cub close to her, she tramped down the mountain. She crossed the Brooks River, and jogged along the shore of Lake Naknek, around the rocky foot of Mount Katolinat and out across the marshland.

She passed a moose. She walked under clouds of swallows, and trotted for miles and miles to the shores of the Margot River.

On the riverbank she twitched her golden ears and watched hordes of salmon swim by. Then, with a loud splash, she dove and came up with a fish. She never went back to the bears of the Brooks River.

CHECK FOR UNDERSTANDING

1. What was the favorite food of the grizzly bears, and how did they get it?
2. In what way did Golden Ears become a problem for the park ranger?
3. What do you think happened to make Golden Ears's cub disappear?
4. If Golden Ears decided to return to Brooks River, what do you think would happen to her and her cub?

WRITE ABOUT

"The Grizzly Bear with the Golden Ears"
 This story gives you facts about grizzly bears. Write a paragraph that tells what most grizzly bears look like and what they eat.

GRIZZLY BEAR

by MARY AUSTIN

If you ever, ever meet a grizzly bear,
You must never, never, never ask him where
He is going,
Or what he is doing;
For if you ever, ever, dare
To stop a grizzly bear,
You will never meet another grizzly bear.

Following Directions

What do you need before you make a sandwich, play a new game, or write a report? You need a set of **directions**, the steps that tell you what to do. If you can read and follow directions, you can do many things that call for certain steps. To make a sandwich, you do the steps in order. You can't butter a slice of bread <u>after</u> you put on the filling! Playing a new game means learning its rules and following them. You need to read through the directions before you can play a board game, or you will be confused. Writing a report has special steps, too. You must pick a topic, read about it, make notes on it, write up the notes, edit them, and make a final copy. When you use directions, always do these three things:

- preview—read through—the directions
- follow the directions in order
- do not skip any steps in the directions

The examples that follow will tell you why.

Carl moved to a new city. He wanted to find the nearest library, so he asked a neighbor for directions. Look at the directions that Mrs. Hamill wrote down for Carl at the top of page 189.

Walk up First Street to Fifth Avenue.
Turn right and walk two blocks.
Turn left on Third Street and walk three blocks past the traffic light.
The library is closed on Wednesdays.

Carl started out for the library Wednesday morning without first reading all the way through the directions. What do you think happened? The library was closed! Carl should have previewed the directions before using them.

Ellen's class wrote these directions for drawing a map of their state.

Make an outline of the entire state on your piece of paper.
Draw a star and write the name of the capital city next to it.
Draw large dots to locate the big cities.
Write in the names of the cities.
Draw in the major rivers and lakes.
Write in the names of the rivers and lakes.

Ellen did not leave much time to draw her map. She decided to skip the first step. She drew a star and some large dots for the cities in her part of the state. Then she thought that she could save time by writing in the names of the rivers and lakes before drawing them on the map. Soon, Ellen looked at her map closely. It was a mess! What had Ellen done wrong?

First, she skipped a step in the directions. She did not make an outline of the state, so she could only fit part of the state on her paper. Second, she did not follow the directions in order. Instead of drawing the rivers and lakes first, she printed their names where she thought they belonged. But there was little room left for the sketches of the lakes. By starting over and following the directions carefully, Ellen finally made a useful map.

Now you can see why it is important to preview directions, to follow them in order, and to not skip any steps in the directions.

You know how important it is to be able to read and follow directions. You can't make a peanut butter and banana sandwich without following the steps in the right order. For example, the peanut butter must go on the bread before the banana.

The pictures show four steps needed to make a peanut butter and banana sandwich. Write a set of directions that describes all of the steps given in the pictures.

YAGUA DAYS

by CRUZ MARTEL

How do you feel about rainy days? Do they make you unhappy because they keep you from doing things you enjoy? Adan feels this way until he learns a rainy day is a *yagua* day.

What is a yagua day? Where does Adan learn what a yagua day is?

It was raining steadily on the Lower East Side. From the doorway of his parents' *bodega,* Adan Riera watched a car splash the sidewalk.

School had ended for the summer two days ago. And for two days it had rained! Adan wanted to play in East River Park. But with so much rain, about the only thing a boy could do was watch the cars splash by.

Of course, he could help his father. Adan enjoyed working in the bodega. He liked the smells of the fruits and the different colors of the vegetables. But today he would rather be in the park.

Jorge came in, slapping water off his hat. He smiled. "Why the long face, Adan?"

"Rainy days are terrible days."

"No, they're wonderful days. They're *yagua* days."

"Stop teasing, Jorge. Yesterday you told me the vegetables and fruits in the bodega are grown in trucks. What's a yagua day?"

---

bodega (bō dā′gə), a Puerto Rican grocery store.
yagua (jä′ gwä), the outer covering of a palm leaf.

"This day is a yagua day. And Puerto Rican vegetables and fruits *are* grown in trucks. Why, I have a truck myself. Every day I water it!"

Adan's mother and father came in from the back.

"*Hola,* Jorge. You look wet," said Adan's father.

"I feel wetter. But it's a wonderful feeling. It's a yagua-day feeling!"

His father and mother liked Jorge. They had grown up together in Puerto Rico.

"So you've been telling Adan about yagua days?"

"*Sí.* Here's a letter for you from *Corral Viejo,* where we all had some of the best yagua days."

Adan's father read the letter. "Good news!" My brother Ulise wants *Mami,* Adan, and me to visit him on his *finca* for two weeks. It's been years since I've been to Puerto Rico," he added thoughtfully.

---

hola (ō′ la), hello.   *mami* (mä′ mē), mommy.
sí (sē), yes.   *finca* (fēn′ kä), plantation.
Corral Viejo (kō rôl′ vē ye′ hō), old corral.

"Adan's never been there," replied his mother. "We can ask my brother to take care of the bodega. Adan will meet his family in the mountains at last."

Adan clapped his hands. "Puerto Rico! Who cares about the rain!"

Jorge smiled. "Maybe you'll even have a few yagua days. *Hasta luego. Y que gocen mucho!*"

Tío Ulise met them at the airport in *Ponce*.

"Welcome to Puerto Rico, Adan."

Stocky Uncle Ulise had tiny blue eyes in a round, red face and big, strong arms. Adan was excited after his first plane ride. He hugged Uncle Ulise even harder than Uncle Ulise hugged him.

---

hasta luego (ä′ stä lo͞o we′ gō), till we meet again; good-by.
y que gocen mucho (ē ke gō′ sen mo͞o′ chō), and have fun.
tío (tē′ ō), uncle.
Ponce (pôn′ sä), a city in southern Puerto Rico.

"Come, we'll drive to Corral Viejo." He winked at Adan's father. "I'm sorry you didn't arrive yesterday. Yesterday was a wonderful yagua day."

"Tío Ulise, you know about yagua days, too?"

"Sure. They're my favorite days."

"But wouldn't today be a good yagua day?"

"The worst. The sun's out!"

In an old jeep, they rode up into the mountains.

"Look!" said Uncle Ulise, pointing at a river jumping rocks. "Your mother and father, Jorge, and I played in that river when we were children."

They bounced up a hill to a cluster of bright houses. Many people were outside.

"This is your family, Adan," said Uncle Ulise.

Everyone crowded around the jeep. There were old and young people, and blond-haired, brown-haired, and black-haired people. There were dark-skinned and light-skinned people and blue-eyed, brown-eyed, and green-eyed people. Adan had not known there were so many people in his family. Uncle Ulise's wife, Carmen, hugged Adan and kissed both his cheeks.

The whole family sat under wide trees and ate rice, pork, vegetables, and dumplings. Adan talked and sang until his voice turned to a squeak. He ate until his stomach almost popped a pants button. Afterward he fell asleep under a big mosquito net. He was asleep even before the sun had gone down behind the mountains.

In the morning Uncle Ulise called out, "Adan, everyone ate all the food in the house. Let's get more."

"From a bodega?"

"No, *mi amor*—from my finca near the top of the mountain."

"You can drive a tractor and a plow on the mountain?"

Tía Carmen smiled with her eyes. "We don't need tractors and plows on our finca."

"I don't understand."

"Come on. You will."

Adan and his parents, Aunt Carmen, and Uncle Ulise hiked up the mountain beside a splashy stream.

Near the top they walked through groves of fruit trees.

mi amor (mē ä mor'), my love.
tía (tē' ä), aunt.

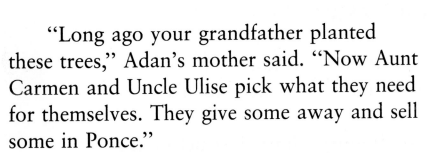

"Long ago your grandfather planted these trees," Adan's mother said. "Now Aunt Carmen and Uncle Ulise pick what they need for themselves. They give some away and sell some in Ponce."

"Let's work!" said Aunt Carmen.

Sitting on his father's shoulders, Adan picked oranges. Swinging a hooked stick, he pulled down *mangós*. Finally, gripping a very long pole, he struck down coconuts.

"How do we get all the food down the mountain?" he asked.

"Watch," said Aunt Carmen. She whistled loudly.

Adan saw a patch of white moving in the trees. A horse with a golden mane appeared.

Uncle Ulise fed him a mangó. The horse twitched his ears and munched the delicious fruit loudly.

---

mangó (man gō′), a sweet tropical fruit, golden when ripe.

"Palomo will help us carry all the fruit and vegetables we're picking," Adan's mother said.

Back at the house, Adan gave Palomo another mangó.

"Palomo will go back to the finca now," his father said. "It's got all it wants to eat there."

Uncle Ulise rubbed his knee.

"What's the matter?" asked Adan's mother.

"My knee. It always hurts just before the rain comes."

Adan looked at the cloudless sky. "But it's not going to rain."

"Yes, it will. My knee never lies. It'll rain tonight. Maybe tomorrow. Say! When it does, it'll be a yagua day!"

In the morning Adan woke up feeling cozy under his mosquito net. He heard rain banging on the metal roof. He jumped out of bed and got a big surprise. His mother and father, Uncle Ulise, and Aunt Carmen were on the porch wearing bathing suits.

"Come, Adan," his father said. "It's a wonderful yagua day. Put on your bathing suit!"

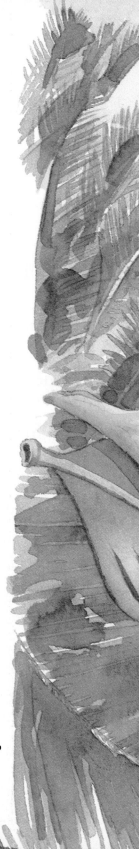

In the forest he heard shouts and swishing noises in the rain. Racing into a clearing, he saw boys and girls shooting down a runway of grass. Then they quickly disappeared over a rock ledge.

Uncle Ulise picked up a canoe-like object from the grass. "This is yagua, Adan. It fell from this palm tree."

"And this is what we do with it," said his father. He ran, then belly flopped on the yagua. He skimmed down the grass, sailed up into the air, and vanished over the ledge. His mother found another yagua and did the same.

"*Papi!* Mami!"

Uncle Ulise laughed. "Don't worry, Adan. They won't hurt themselves. The river is down there. It pools beneath the ledge. The rain turns the grass butter-slick so you can zip into the water. That's what makes it a yagua day! Come and join us!"

That day Adan found out what fun a yagua day is!

Two weeks later Adan lifted a box of mangós off the truck back in New York.

"Hola! Welcome home!"

Adan smiled at Jorge. "Why do you look sad, *compadre?*"

"Too much mail! Too much sun!"

"What you need is a yagua day."

"So you know what a yagua day is?"

"I had six yagua days in Puerto Rico."

"You went over the ledge?"

"Of course."

papi (pä′ pē), daddy.
compadre (kom pä′ dre), pal.

"Into the river?"

"Sí! Sí! Into the river. Sliding on yaguas!"

"Two-wheeled or four-wheeled yaguas?"

Adan laughed. "Yaguas don't have wheels. They come from palm trees."

"I thought they come from panel trucks like mine."

"Nothing grows in trucks, Jorge. These mangós and oranges come from trees. Compadre, wake up. Don't you know?"

Jorge laughed. "Come, let's talk with your parents. I want to hear all about your visit to Corral Viejo!"

CHECK FOR UNDERSTANDING

1. Where did Adan finally learn what a yagua day is?
2. What is a yagua day? Describe what Adan and his family did on a yagua day.
3. Why was the day that Adan arrived in Puerto Rico *not* a good yagua day?
4. What are the land and weather like in the part of Puerto Rico Adan visited?
5. Compare sliding on yaguas to sledding on snow. How are they alike? How are they different?

Weather Is Full of the Nicest Sounds

by AILEEN FISHER

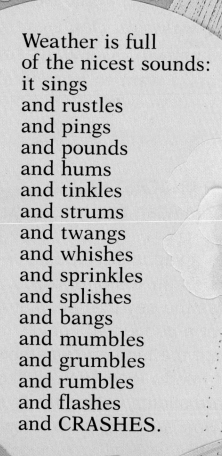

Weather is full
of the nicest sounds:
it sings
and rustles
and pings
and pounds
and hums
and tinkles
and strums
and twangs
and whishes
and sprinkles
and splishes
and bangs
and mumbles
and grumbles
and rumbles
and flashes
and CRASHES.

I wonder
if thunder
frightens a bee,
a mouse in her house,
a bird in a tree,
a bear
or a hare
or a fish in the sea?
Not *me!*

205

Cause and Effect

Many events in a story happen because of other events. What happens is called the **effect,** and what makes it happen is the **cause.** Read this paragraph from the story "Yagua Days." What effect does the rainy weather have on Adan?

School had ended for the summer two days ago. And for two days it had rained! Adan wanted to play in the East River Park. But with so much rain, about the only thing a boy could do was watch the cars splash by.

The rainy weather causes Adan to be disappointed. It keeps him from playing in the park. The rain <u>causes</u> Adan's bad mood. His bad mood is the <u>effect</u>.

In "Yagua Days" Adan's father receives a letter from his brother. Because of this letter, Adan's family travels to Puerto Rico. To find the cause and effect in these events, ask, "What happens?" and "What makes it happen?" The answer is that the letter, the <u>cause</u>, makes the trip, the <u>effect</u>, happen.

Sometimes a number of events can have just one effect. Read the four sentences at the top of page 207 based on events in "Yagua Days." Then decide what effect these events have on Adan.

Adan and his family visited Corral Viejo.
Adan talked and sang and ate.
He picked mangós and coconuts.
He slid down the grass on a yagua.

The events describe how much fun Adan had at Corral Viejo. Together, these events had one effect. They changed Adan from a sad to a happy boy.

Think about what happens, and what makes it happen, as you read these sentences. Try to identify the cause, or causes, and the effect in each group.

Suzanne put too much pepper in the sauce.
Everyone at the table began to sneeze.

The wind whipped the trees.
Rain fell in lashing drops.
The air turned very cold.
We put off the picnic until next week.

Do you see how one thing, or more than one thing, can cause something else to happen? What caused everyone at the table to sneeze? It was the pepper. In the second group of sentences, three causes are given. The wind, rain, and cold caused the picnic to be put off.

What are the causes and effect in this paragraph?

The Gold Team won the game. They practiced all week. Everyone got plenty of rest. The coach was full of encouraging words.

SAM, BANGS AND MOONSHINE

by EVALINE NESS

Make-believe can be fun, but too much make-believe can mean trouble. After sending her friend Thomas into danger with her make-believe, Samantha must take another look at where make-believe ends and real begins.
What happened to Thomas because of Sam's make-believe ideas?

On a small island, near a large harbor, there once lived a fisher's little daughter (named Samantha, but always called Sam), who had the reckless habit of lying.

Not even the sailors home from the sea could tell stranger stories than Sam. Not even the ships in the harbor, with curious cargoes from giraffes to gerbils, claimed more wonders than Sam did.

Sam said her mother was a mermaid. But everyone knew she was dead.

Sam said she had a fierce lion at home, and a baby kangaroo. (Actually, what she *really* had was an old wise cat called Bangs.)

Sam even said that Bangs could talk if and when he wanted to.

Sam said this. Sam said that. But whatever Sam said you could never believe.

Even Bangs yawned and shook his head when she said the ragged old rug on the doorstep was a chariot drawn by dragons.

Early one morning, before Sam's father left in his fishing boat to be gone all day, he hugged Sam hard and said, "Today, for a change, talk REAL, not MOONSHINE. MOONSHINE spells trouble."

Sam promised. But while she washed the dishes, made the beds, and swept the floor, she wondered what he meant. When she asked Bangs to explain REAL and MOONSHINE, Bangs jumped on her shoulder and purred, "MOONSHINE is flummadiddle. REAL is the opposite."

Sam decided that Bangs made no sense whatever.

When the sun made a golden star on the cracked window, Sam knew it was time to expect Thomas.

Thomas lived in the tall grand house on the hill. Thomas had two cows in the barn, twenty-five sheep, a bicycle with a basket, and a jungle gym on the lawn. But most important of all, Thomas believed every word Sam said.

At the same time every day, Thomas rode his bicycle down the hill to Sam's house and begged to see her baby kangaroo.

Every day Sam told Thomas it had just "stepped out." She sent Thomas everywhere to find it. She sent him to the tallest trees where, she said, it was visiting owls. Or perhaps it was up in the old windmill, grinding corn for its evening meal.

"It might be," said Sam, "in the lighthouse tower, warning ships at sea."

"Or maybe," she said, "it's asleep on the sand. Somewhere, anywhere on the beach."

Wherever Sam sent Thomas, he went. He climbed up trees. He ran down steps. He scoured the beach. But he never found Sam's baby kangaroo.

While Thomas searched, Sam sat in her chariot and was drawn by dragons to faraway secret worlds.

Today, when Thomas arrived, Sam said, "That baby kangaroo just left to visit my mermaid mother. She lives in a cave behind Blue Rock."

Sam watched Thomas race away on his bicycle over the narrow strand that stretched to a massive blue rock in the distance. Then she sat down in her chariot. Bangs came out of the house and sat down beside Sam. With his head turned in the direction of Thomas, Bangs said, "When the tide comes up, it covers the road to Blue Rock. Tide rises early today."

Sam looked at Bangs for a minute. Then she said, "Pardon me while I go to the moon."

Bangs stood up. He stretched his front legs. Then he stretched his back legs. Slowly he stalked away from Sam toward Blue Rock.

Suddenly Sam had no desire to go to the moon. Or any other place either. She just sat in her chariot and thought about Bangs and Thomas.

She was so busy thinking, she was unaware of thick, muddy clouds that blocked out the sun. Nor did she hear the menacing rumble of thunder. She was almost knocked off the doorstep when a sudden gust of wind drove torrents of rain against her face.

Sam leaped into the house and slammed the door. She went to the window to look at Blue Rock. She could see nothing through the gray ribbed curtain of rain. She wondered where Thomas was. She wondered where Bangs was. Sam stood there looking at nothing. She tried to swallow the lump that rose in her throat.

The murky light in the room deepened to black. Sam was still at the window when her father burst into the house. Water streamed from his hat and oozed from his boots. Sam ran screaming, "Bangs and Thomas are out on the rock! Blue Rock! Bangs and Thomas!"

Her father turned quickly and ran out the door. He ordered Sam to stay in the house.

"And pray that the tide hasn't covered the rock!" he yelled.

When her father had gone, Sam sat down. She listened to the rain hammer on the tin roof. Then suddenly it stopped. Sam closed her eyes and mouth, tight. She waited in the quiet room. It seemed to her that she waited forever.

At last she heard her father's footsteps outside. She flung open the door and said one word: "Bangs?"

Sam's father shook his head.

"He was washed away," he said. "But I found Thomas on the rock. I brought him back in the boat. He's home now, safe in bed. Can you tell me how all this happened?"

Sam started to explain, but sobs choked her. She cried so hard that it was a long time before her father understood everything. Finally, Sam's father said, "Go to bed now. But before you go to sleep, Sam, tell yourself the difference between REAL and MOONSHINE."

Sam went to her room and crept into bed. With her eyes wide open she thought about REAL and MOONSHINE.

MOONSHINE was a mermaid-mother, a fierce lion, a chariot drawn by dragons, and certainly a baby kangaroo. It was all flummadiddle just as Bangs had told her. Or *had* he told her? Wouldn't her father say that a cat's talking was MOONSHINE?

REAL was no mother at all. REAL was her father and Bangs. And now there wasn't even Bangs. Tears welled up in Sam's eyes again. They ran down into her ears, making a scratching noise. Sam sat up and blew her nose. The scratching was not in her ears. It was at the window. As Sam stared at the black oblong, two enormous yellow eyes appeared and stared back. Sam sprang from her bed. She opened the window. There sat Bangs, his coat a sodden mess.

"Oh, Bangs!" cried Sam. She grabbed and smothered him with kisses. "What happened to you?"

In a few words, Bangs told her that one moment he was on the rock with Thomas and the next he was lying at the foot of the lighthouse tower a mile away. All done by waves.

"Nasty stuff, water," Bangs grumbled, as he washed himself from his ears to his feet.

Sam patted Bangs. "Well, at least it's not flummadiddle. . . ." Sam paused. She looked up to see her father standing in the doorway.

"Look! Bangs is home!" shouted Sam.

"Hello Bangs. What's not flummadiddle?" asked Sam's father.

"Bangs! And you! And Thomas!" answered Sam. "Oh, Daddy! I'll always know the difference between REAL and MOONSHINE now. Bangs and Thomas were almost lost because of MOONSHINE. Bangs told me."

"He *told* you?" questioned Sam's father.

"Well, he would have *if* he could talk," said Sam. Then she added sadly, "I know cats can't talk like people, but I almost believed I *did* have a baby kangaroo."

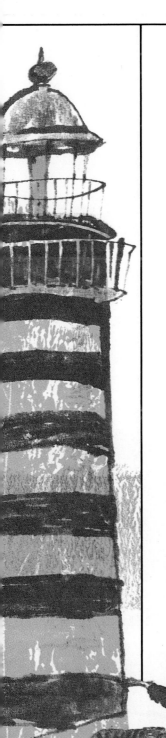

Her father looked steadily at her.

"There's good MOONSHINE and bad MOONSHINE," he said. "The important thing is to know the difference." He kissed Sam good night and left the room.

When he had closed the door, Sam said, "You know, Bangs, I might just keep my chariot."

This time Bangs did not yawn and shake his head. Instead he licked her hand. He waited until she got into bed; then he curled up at her feet and went to sleep.

The next morning Sam opened her eyes to see an incredible thing! Hopping toward her on its hind legs was a small, elegant, large-eyed animal with a long tail like a lion's. Behind it strolled Bangs and her father.

"A baby kangaroo!" shouted Sam. "Where did you find it?"

"It is *not* a baby kangaroo," said Sam's father. "It's a gerbil. I found it on an African banana boat in the harbor."

"Now Thomas can see a baby kangaroo at last!" Sam squealed with joy.

Sam's father interrupted her. "Stop the MOONSHINE, Sam. Call it by its REAL name. Anyway, Thomas won't come by today. He's sick in bed with laryngitis. He can't even talk. Also, his bicycle got lost in the storm."

Sam looked down at the gerbil. Gently she stroked its tiny head. Without raising her eyes, she said, "Daddy, do you think I should *give* the gerbil to Thomas?"

Sam's father said nothing. Bangs licked his tail.

Suddenly Sam hollered, "Come on, Bangs!"

She jumped out of bed and slipped into her shoes. As she grabbed her coat, she picked up the gerbil and ran from the house with Bangs at her heels. Sam did not stop running until she stood at the side of Thomas's bed.

Very carefully she placed the gerbil on Thomas's stomach. The little animal sat straight up on its long hind legs. It gazed directly at Thomas with its immense round eyes.

"Whaaaaaaaaaa sis name?" wheezed
Thomas.

"MOONSHINE," answered Sam, as she
gave Bangs a big, wide smile.

CHECK FOR UNDERSTANDING

1. Explain the difference between real and moonshine.
2. Give three examples of Sam's moonshine.
3. What happened to Thomas because of Sam's make-believe?
4. Did Bangs really talk to Sam? What do you think was happening when Sam thought Bangs was talking to her?
5. Why do you think Sam gave Thomas the gerbil?

WRITE ABOUT *"Sam, Bangs and Moonshine"*
Sam's father tells her: "There's good MOONSHINE and bad MOONSHINE. The important thing is to know the difference." Write a paragraph explaining how good moonshine and bad moonshine are different. Give one or two examples of each in your paragraph.

Daniel's Duck

by CLYDE ROBERT BULLA

Have you ever made something you were proud of? How would you have felt if people laughed at what you made? Daniel is hurt when people laugh at something he's made, until one special person gives him a new way to see the laughter.

What does Daniel's brother, Jeff, say about Daniel's carving when it is half-finished? Why did Mr. Pettigrew, the woodcarver, laugh at Daniel's duck carving?

220

Jeff and Daniel were brothers. They lived in a cabin on a mountain in Tennessee. Jeff had a good knife, and he could carve things out of wood. He made a dish, a cup, and a spoon. "Some day," Jeff said, "I want to carve an animal like Henry Pettigrew's."

Henry Pettigrew lived in the valley, and although Jeff and Daniel had never met him, they had seen his work. Some said he was the best woodcarver in Tennessee. All his animals looked real; his birds looked as if they could fly, and his horses looked as if they could run.

"I want to carve an animal, too," said Daniel.

"You're not old enough," Jeff told him.

"Yes, I am," said Daniel. "I could carve one if I had a good knife and some wood."

"It takes more than a good knife and some wood," said Jeff. "Animals are hard to do, and you have to know how."

"I know how," answered Daniel.

"Let's see if you do," said his father, and he gave Daniel a knife like Jeff's and a block of wood.

It was winter, and the nights were long.

"This is a good time to sit by the fire and carve," said Jeff. "I'm going to make something for the spring fair."

Every spring there was a fair in the valley. It was a time for people to meet after the long winter and show what they had made. Sometimes they also sold or traded things.

On winter nights Father made moccasins to take to the fair, and Mother cut pieces of cloth which she sewed together into a quilt.

"I'm going to make a box," said Jeff, "and carve little moons on the lid." He looked at his brother. "You haven't done anything with your block of wood. What are you going to make?"

"I have to think," said Daniel.

Days went by. Then he began to carve.

"What are you making?" asked Jeff.

"You'll see," said Daniel.

One night Jeff looked at what Daniel was carving. He saw a neck and a head and a wing. "Now I see," he said. "It's a bird."

"It's a duck," said Daniel.

"You're not doing it right," Jeff told him. "Its head is on backward."

"I want it that way," said Daniel. "My duck is looking back."

"That's no way to do it," said Jeff.

Father interrupted. "Let him do it his way."

Spring came, and it was time for the fair. Mother had finished her quilt, and Father had made three pairs of moccasins.

Jeff's box was done. "It took a long time," he said.

"My duck took a long time, too," said Daniel.

"Are you sure you want to take it to the fair?" asked Jeff.

"Yes," said Daniel.

They went down the mountain in a wagon, and Father drove the horses into town. People were everywhere. Father took the quilt, the moccasins, Jeff's box, and Daniel's duck, and he left them at the hall, a long house in the middle of town. "This is where the show will be," said Father. "People are getting it ready now."

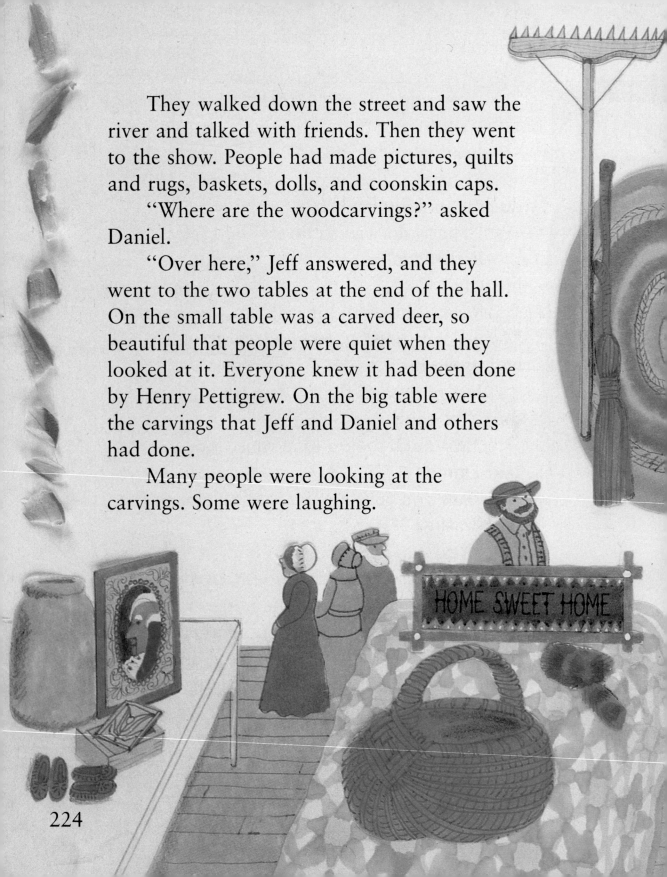

They walked down the street and saw the river and talked with friends. Then they went to the show. People had made pictures, quilts and rugs, baskets, dolls, and coonskin caps.

"Where are the woodcarvings?" asked Daniel.

"Over here," Jeff answered, and they went to the two tables at the end of the hall. On the small table was a carved deer, so beautiful that people were quiet when they looked at it. Everyone knew it had been done by Henry Pettigrew. On the big table were the carvings that Jeff and Daniel and others had done.

Many people were looking at the carvings. Some were laughing.

224

"What are they laughing at?" asked Daniel, but Jeff didn't answer.

Someone said, "Look at the duck!"

More people came to look, and they were laughing, too. Someone else said, "That duck is so funny!"

Now Daniel knew they were laughing at his duck. At first he wanted to hide, but then he was angry. He went to the table, picked up his duck, and ran out of the hall with it.

Someone was running after him, but Daniel ran faster, until he came to the river. He wanted to throw the duck as far as he could.

But before he could, a man grabbed his arm and asked. "What are you doing with that duck?"

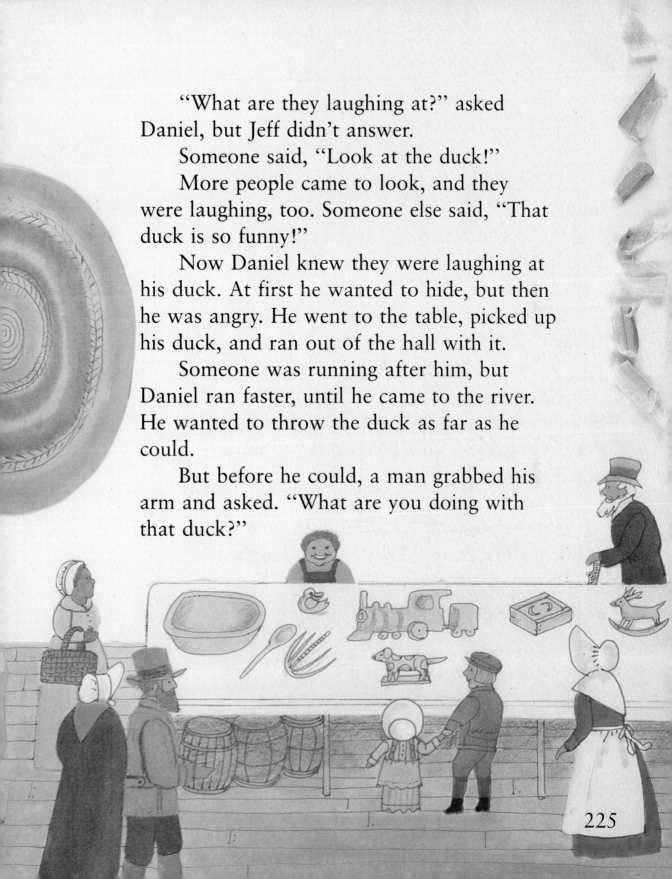

225

"I'm going to throw it in the river!" said Daniel.

"You can't do that," said the man.

"I can if I want to," said Daniel. "It's mine."

"Did you make it?" asked the man, and he let go of Daniel's arm.

"Yes," said Daniel.

"Then why were you going to throw it away?"

"They all laughed at it," said Daniel.

"Listen to me," said the man. "There are different ways of laughing. The people *liked* your duck; they laughed because they liked it."

"No. It's ugly," said Daniel.

"It *isn't* ugly. It's a good duck, and it made me feel happy. That's why I laughed." But the man wasn't laughing now. "You're hot and tired," he said. "Come and rest in the shade."

They sat under a tree. "Would you sell your duck?" asked the man.

"Who would buy it?" asked Daniel.

"I might think of someone," answered the man.

A boy and girl came up to them. "How are you, Mr. Pettigrew?" they asked.

"I'm fine," he answered, and when the boy and girl walked on, Daniel looked at the man again.

"You're Henry Pettigrew!"

"Yes," he said. "I'm a woodcarver, too."

"I know," said Daniel, and he looked down at his duck. It wasn't ugly; it was a good duck. Henry Pettigrew had said so, and he was the best woodcarver in Tennessee!

CHECK FOR UNDERSTANDING

1. Why was Henry Pettigrew well known in Tennessee?
2. What did Jeff say about Daniel's carving when it was half-finished?
3. What happened at the fair that made Daniel run to the river?
4. What new outlook did Mr. Pettigrew give Daniel about the carving of the duck?
5. Why was it important to Daniel that it was Mr. Pettigrew who said his duck carving was good?

THINK ABOUT IT

Think about the characters in the stories you have read. How were they stuck in their way of doing things? Who or what gave them a new outlook?

- What made Mr. Breton unhappy that he couldn't seem to change?
- What became a habit that Golden Ears couldn't seem to break?
- How did Adan feel about rainy days before and after his trip?
- How did Sam change her definition of *moonshine*?
- What words were used to describe Daniel's carving, and which ones changed his outlook about it?

After reading and thinking about the stories, how much would you say people are able to change?

WRITE ABOUT IT

Describe a situation in which you either gave a friend a new outlook, or a friend gave you a new outlook. Write a paragraph explaining how you or your friend were stuck. Be specific in telling how the new outlook helped you or your friend change.

READ ABOUT IT

Millie Cooper, 3B by Charlotte Herman. E. P. Dutton & Co., Inc., 1985. Millie is trying to hold back tears when her spelling grade is lowered because of an ink blot. She thinks everything would be different if she just had one of those new ballpoint pens.

Journey to the Bright Kingdom by Elizabeth Winthrop. Holiday House, 1979. Kiyo's blind mother is granted her wish to see her daughter's face once again by the mice of Kakure-sato. After that, she is eagerly ready to face the world and her tasks.

Stage Fright by Ann N. Martin. Holiday House, 1984. Sara, who is shy, hates big groups and talking in school. When her class presents a play, she works hard and becomes a part of the group.

The Adventures of Ali Baba Bernstein by Johanna Hurwitz. William Morrow & Co., Inc., 1985. David Bernstein is around eight when he decides to name himself Ali Baba. This will make his life more exciting, he thinks.

4

PREDICAMENTS AND PUZZLES

Have you ever gotten rocks in your socks? Have you ever wanted to solve a mystery like a detective? If you answered "yes" to either of these questions, you are going to enjoy this unit of "predicaments and puzzles."

As you read this unit, think about the author's purpose in writing each story. Is the author trying to make you laugh? Is the author trying to teach you something? Is the author trying to get you to solve a mystery?

If you were an ox with rocks in your socks, what would you do? One thing you probably should not do is listen to a fox.

What is the fox's first suggestion for getting the rocks out of the ox's socks? What should the ox have done in the first place?

"There Are Rocks in My Socks!" Said the Ox to the Fox

by PATRICIA THOMAS

"There are rocks
In my socks,"
Said the ox
To the fox.
"Bumpy old,
Lumpy old,
Clumpy old rocks . . .
Pinchy
And squinchy
Whenever one walks.
I feel very grumpy
With rocks in my socks!"

"See here,
My dear steer,"
Said the fox
To the ox.
"Why don't you stop grumping
And take out the rocks?
I must say I've noticed, the longer one talks,
The less time one has for taking out rocks."

"But sir, there's no way,"
Said the ox
To the fox,
"To get rid of these rocks
That are inside my socks.
With my shoes underneath,
    my feet firmly on top . . .
I see no way at all of removing the rocks."

"Let me think,"
Said the fox
To the ox
With a wink.
"There MUST be a way to get rocks out of
socks.

Eureka!
I have it! Just do a flip-flop . . .
Put your legs in the air, so your feet aren't
    on top
Of the rocks,
Which will then slide right out of your socks.
It's a good thing I'm clever!"
Said the fox
To the ox.

"Yes, indeed, you are clever,"
Said the ox
To the fox.
"If I do a flip-flop
So my feet aren't on top,
Then, the rocks
Will come tumbling right out of my socks!"

Flip . . . Zip . . . Flop . . . Plop!

"There's a tack
In my back,"
Said the ox
To the fox.
"A prickly old,
Tickly old,
Stickly old tack!

234

I really don't need
This particular tack.
If I found it was missing
I'd not wish it back.
Furthermore, those rocks
Haven't budged from my socks!"
Said the ox
To the fox.

Said the fox
To the ox,
"There's no need to sigh.
I'll have it all solved in the blink of an eye.
Quick!
Flick
Your tail 'neath your back,
And you'll knock aside quickly that prickly
    old tack!
You're lucky I'm here,"
Said the fox
To the ox.

"Yes, you're a great help,"
Said the ox
To the fox.

235

"With a swish of my tail,
I'll give that old tack
A good whack
That will knock it
From under my back!"

Swish . . . Whish-h-h . . . Whump . . . Thump!

"There's a rail
On my tail,"
Said the ox
To the fox.
"A knotty old,
Cloddy old,
Rotty old rail.
And I'm sure if this rail
Were placed on a scale,
The whole thing would weigh just as much as
    a whale!
I venture to state
That in time one would hate
The very great
Weight
Of a rail
On one's tail!

236

Not to mention the tack
That is still in my back
And all of the rocks
That are still in my socks!"
Said the ox
To the fox.

"There, there,
Don't despair,"
Said the fox
To the ox.
"For it's true, don't you see,
(I'm sure you'll agree)
You've no more to fear as long as you've me.
Your troubles are over, I swear it is true—
For what else could possibly happen to you?"

Zzzz . . . Buzzz . . . Flit . . . Sit!

Said the ox
To the fox,
"Thank you, my friend,
For your faith that my troubles
Will come to an end.

237

Perhaps you are right
To make light of my plight,
But it seems that the end
Is not yet quite in sight.
For here I remain
With rocks
In my socks
And a tack
In my back
And a rail
On my tail.
And if that's not enough, I believe a large bee
Has decided to stop and rest on my knee!
That makes me uneasy,
In fact, somewhat queasy,
For a large bee is a thing
With a very large sting!"

Said the fox
To the ox,
"Yes, it does seem to me
You'd be much better off without that
    large bee.

However—
Because I'm so clever,
I instantly see
A way to remove that large bee
From your knee.
Just be quick!
Kick
Your toes
In the air toward your nose,
Which will shake your knee free
Of that unwelcome bee."

"Of course,"
Said the ox,
"How stupid of me!
It's remarkably easy
To shake off a bee!"

Flick . . . Kick . . . Zap . . . Whap!

Said the ox
To the fox,
"You've observed, I suppose,
That I seem to have kicked myself hard
    in the nose.

239

Meanwhile, the large bee,
Not choosing to flee,
Has been startled instead into stinging my knee.
(Which is, I confess, quite unpleasant for me.)
What's more, with these rocks
Still stuck in my socks
And the tack in my back
And the rail
On my tail . . .
I do believe it is fair to state
My situation is less than great."

Skippety . . . Hippety-Hop . . . Stop.

"My word," said the bird,
"My eyes must be blurred.
I've never seen anything quite so absurd!
A big, grown-up ox
With his back
On a tack
And a rail
On his tail
And a bee
On his knee
Gives his own nose a whack!
(Please don't go, Mr. Fox.)

As for you, Mr. Ox,
Would you care to relate
How you got in this state?"

"It's a rather long story,"
Said the ox
To the bird.
"It is hard to explain
Everything that's occurred.
I believe it began with my friend here,
    the fox,
Who's an expert at getting rocks out of
    one's socks."

Said the bird
To the ox,
"I really must say,
You're going about it in a very strange way.
Why not simply roll over,
Lift your back off that tack?
Then just slide your tail
Out from under the rail . . .
And straighten your knee,
Which, so obviously,
Will set the bee
Free."

241

Mumble . . . Tumble . . . Roll . . . "Bless
　　my soul!"

"Now, take off your shoes
Then take off your socks
(Try wiggling your toes!)
Then dump out the rocks.
Next, put back each sock
And put back each shoe . . .
Which is all, Mr. Ox,
That you needed to do."

"Is it true what I've heard?"
Said the ox
To the bird.
"All I needed to do to get rid of these rocks
Was to take off my shoes and to empty
　　my socks?"

"Of course," said the bird.

Jiggle . . . Wiggle . . .
Bump, bump, bump . . .
Thump!
Whump!
Lump!

242

"I believe," said the ox,
"It might well be said
That my friend, the fox,
Has rocks on his head!"

CHECK FOR UNDERSTANDING

1. How did having rocks in his socks make the ox feel?
2. What was the fox's first suggestion for getting the rocks out of the ox's socks?
3. How did the ox get the rail on its tail?
4. How did the ox try to get rid of the bee? What happened as a result?
5. What should the ox have done in the first place?

WRITE ABOUT

"There Are Rocks in My Socks!"

The poem uses words that rhyme. Write a funny rhyming poem of your own. You may use any of the following words in your poem, or choose other rhyming words: *dog, frog, log, bog, creep, leap, heap, cat, that, hat.* (Make your poem at least eight lines long.)

243

The Sounds /ā/, /ē/, /ī/, /ō/

> The apes sailed away
>> on the deep green sea
>> in five bright white
>> old row boats.

The words in this sentence have the long vowel sounds /ā/, /ē/, /ī/, and /ō/. You hear the **long a** sound in the words sailed and away. In these words, the long a sound is spelled a_e as in ape, ai as in sailed, and ay as in away.

Here are more long a words.

name	main	today	take
say	place	date	tail

The **long e** sound is heard in the words deep, green, and sea. In these words, long e is spelled with ea as in sea, ee as in green and deep.

Here are more long e words.

money	monkey	eagle	tree
team	sleep	teach	street

The vowel sound of **long i** is heard in the word five. The long i sound can be spelled with i_e as in five and with igh as in bright. It can also be spelled with i as in lion, or y as at the end of a word or word part, as in fly.

Here are more long i words.

fine	lion	slight	my
tight	cry	pine	prize

You hear the vowel sound **long o** in words such as boat, old, and row. Long o can be spelled oa as in boat, o as in old, or ow as in row. Long o can also be spelled o_e as in note.

Here are more long o words.

bone	post	told	yellow
soak	coat	colt	golden

Look for words with the sounds /ā/, /ē/, /ī/, and /ō/ as you read these sentences.

Please take these three kites home with you.
We will fly them tomorrow.

The Case of the
BROKEN WINDOW

by DONALD J. SOBOL

Solving a puzzle is fun when it's a game. But Encyclopedia Brown thinks it's even more fun to solve a puzzling crime.

Why does Chief Brown think the thief is still in the house? What did Encyclopedia Brown figure out about the curved piece of glass?

It was eight thirty at night when John Hall telephoned Chief Brown.

Fifteen minutes later Encyclopedia and his father were driving to Mr. Hall's house. Encyclopedia wore his Halloween pirate's costume. Chief Brown was dressed as a caveman.

"Mr. Hall is giving a costume party tonight," said Chief Brown. "That's the reason for our dressing up. He doesn't want his guests alarmed by the sight of the police."

246

"What happened?" asked Encyclopedia. He had been too excited at going along on a grown-up case to ask questions before now.

"Someone, perhaps a guest, stole a valuable stamp," answered Chief Brown.

Mr. Hall had the largest stamp collection in Idaville. Some of his stamps were worth thousands of dollars.

He was waiting outside his house when Encyclopedia and Chief Brown drove up at quarter past nine.

The two men shook hands and Chief Brown said, "This is my son Leroy. I hope you don't mind that I brought him."

"Your son?" exclaimed Mr. Hall. "Why, I thought he was a real pirate!"

Encyclopedia gritted his teeth and followed the men into the house. They walked past groups of costumed guests and up a flight of stairs.

"In here," said Mr. Hall, entering his study. The room's one window was open. The glass was shattered.

Mr. Hall stopped by the desk, on which lay a stamp album. In a calm voice he told what had happened.

At seven o'clock he had taken the stamp album from the wall safe to enjoy it. At eight o'clock the first guest had arrived and he had gone downstairs. He had locked the door and window, but had left the album out on the desk.

Shortly after eight thirty, he had gone back upstairs to put the album in the safe. He had found the door unlocked and the window broken.

"So far as I can tell at the moment, the only thing missing is the Louis Guinea, a French stamp worth ten thousand dollars," he said.

"The thief probably first sneaked up the stairs and found the door locked," said Chief Brown. "So he went into the backyard and climbed that little tree and broke in. It was already dark and so he was pretty sure no one would see him. He stole the stamp and left by unlocking the door from the inside."

"I quite agree," said Mr. Hall. "The tree is small and shaky. The thief must have decided there was less risk in leaving the room by the staircase."

"That makes him a guest—someone in costume," said Chief Brown. "If he had been questioned on the stairs, he could always say that he had heard a noise and came upstairs to investigate. Has anyone left the party?"

"No, I checked," said Mr. Hall. "All the guests are still here. The thief won't dare call attention to himself by leaving early."

"There is no point to searching everyone," said Chief Brown. "If the thief got wind of a search, he would get rid of the stamp in a second."

"Or worse, destroy it rather than be caught," said Mr. Hall. "That's why I asked you to wear a costume. You can do your work without drawing attention."

Mr. Hall replaced the stamp album in the wall safe.

"I haven't moved anything but the album," he said. "Now, please excuse me. I must rejoin my guests."

After he had gone, Encyclopedia walked to the desk. It was bare except for a pair of tweezers and a bottle of benzine with an eyedropper for finding watermarks. A quartz lamp stood behind the desk chair.

"Leroy, over here," called Chief Brown.

He held up a tiny bit of curved glass. It had fallen among the flat window glass on the carpet.

"It could be from an eyeglass lens," he said. "The thief might have broken his glasses getting into the room."

"Then we better look for a man wearing broken eyeglasses," said Encyclopedia. "Or, if he's taken them off, for someone who squints and bumps into things."

Father and son went downstairs. They decided to separate and meet in the kitchen in half an hour.

Encyclopedia moved slowly among the many colorfully costumed men and women.

A floppy horse brushed past him. "The man in the rear could have glasses on, broken or not," thought Encyclopedia. "But how to find out?"

A man dressed as the great detective Sherlock Holmes—with a deerstalker cap, magnifying glass, and pipe—was reading a poem to a ballerina.

He was reading, however, without the help of eyeglasses or the magnifying glass, and it was the ballerina who squinted.

"No, she's just fluttering her eyelashes," Encyclopedia realized when he moved closer.

A Humpty Dumpty sat on a chair and peered through blinking red eyes.

At the end of half an hour, the boy detective had seen no one with broken eyeglasses or a squint. He headed to the kitchen. On the way he sidestepped a masked man in a cowboy outfit.

Chief Brown was waiting by the stove. "I hope you did better than I," he said. "I struck out."

"Struck . . . that's it, Dad!" exclaimed Encyclopedia. "That bit of curved glass wasn't from an eyeglass lens at all!"

What did Encyclopedia mean?

253

Solution to *The Case of the Broken Window*

Mr. Hall was too upset by the theft of the stamp to notice that something else was missing from his desk.

It was something used in looking at stamps—a magnifying glass.

The thief had broken his magnifying glass when he struck the window with it. He had picked up all the pieces except one from the carpet and dropped them, with the frame, onto the ground below.

To maintain his costume, he had stolen Mr. Hall's magnifying glass along with the stamp.

Mr. Hall found the magnifying glass where Encyclopedia reasoned it was—in the hand of "Sherlock Holmes."

The stolen stamp was found in "Holmes's" wallet.

CHECK FOR UNDERSTANDING

1. Why did Encyclopedia Brown and his father wear costumes to John Hall's house?
2. Why did Chief Brown think the thief was still in the house?
3. What were the detectives looking for when they joined the party downstairs?
4. What did Encyclopedia Brown figure out about the curved piece of glass?
5. Who was the thief?

WRITE ABOUT

"The Case of the Broken Window"

The party at Mr. Hall's house was a costume party. Encyclopedia Brown was dressed as a pirate. Other costumes included a floppy horse, a ballerina, and a cowboy outfit. Write a paragraph telling what each one looked like.

COMPREHENSION

Drawing Conclusions

At the beginning of the story "The Case of the Broken Window," you learned that John Hall has asked Chief Brown and his son Encyclopedia to come to his costume party. A valuable stamp has just been stolen. Why were the Browns invited? Using the fact that the two are good detectives, you can **draw** the **conclusion** that Mr. Hall wants them to find the thief.

At Mr. Hall's house, Encyclopedia and Chief Brown find these clues to the mystery of the missing stamp. What conclusions can you draw about where the thief might be found, using these clues?

> Mr. Hall locked the door and the window when he left the room.
> The window has been broken.
> The door is unlocked.
> The tree outside the window is small and shaky.

These clues tell you that the thief probably broke the window, entered the room, and took the stamp. He or she then unlocked the door and used the staircase to leave, instead of risking climbing down the tree. Your conclusion might be that one of the guests now at Mr. Hall's party is the thief.

As you read a story, you have many chances to draw conclusions. Your conclusions may match what happens in the story. Sometimes you must draw your own conclusions. It is easier to understand a story when you use clues in the story to draw conclusions about what is taking place.

In "The Case of the Broken Window," Encyclopedia's discovery of the bit of curved glass helps him begin his search for the thief. He draws the conclusion that one of the party guests either is wearing broken eyeglasses, or is seeing poorly without using the eyeglasses. When he finds this person, he will find the missing stamp.

In the following example, draw a conclusion by fitting the "clues" together in a way that makes sense.

> Gail is packing a tent into the car trunk.
> Mr. and Mrs. Carlson are putting the cooking equipment into a carton.
> Nick is rolling up the sleeping bags.

Using the clues given, you can conclude that the Carlson family is getting ready to go on a camping trip.

Read the beginning of a story given below. What conclusion can you draw about what has taken place?

> The small white dog ran back and forth in front of the house. It barked furiously. Suddenly a face appeared at a window, and the dog ran up the front steps. It began to jump on its hind legs and bark even louder. A girl opened the door and cried out.

257

WHO CAN COUNT TO TEN?

by FRANCES CARPENTER

King Leopard knows that someday he will die. Before he does, he wants to pick the most clever animal to rule the jungle after him. If you were King Leopard, how would you go about choosing the cleverest animal?

What does King Leopard ask the animals to do? Why do the other animals laugh at the antelope?

CAST

OLD TANKO	ELEPHANT
KING LEOPARD	OX
FROG	RHINOCEROS
RABBIT	CHIMPANZEE
JACKAL	ANTELOPE

PROPS
Crown
Drum
Spear (can be imaginary)

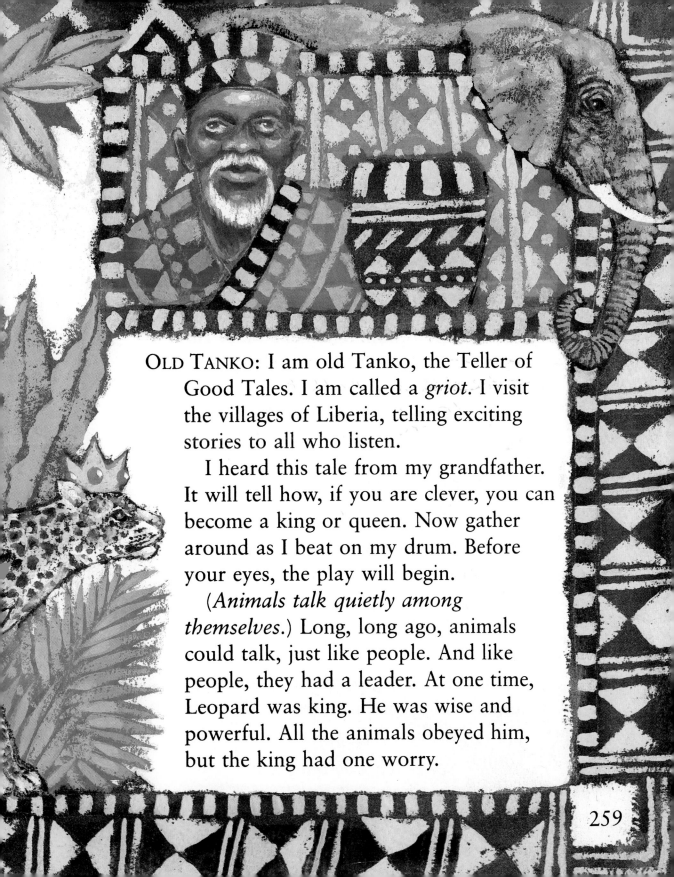

OLD TANKO: I am old Tanko, the Teller of Good Tales. I am called a *griot*. I visit the villages of Liberia, telling exciting stories to all who listen.

I heard this tale from my grandfather. It will tell how, if you are clever, you can become a king or queen. Now gather around as I beat on my drum. Before your eyes, the play will begin.

(*Animals talk quietly among themselves.*) Long, long ago, animals could talk, just like people. And like people, they had a leader. At one time, Leopard was king. He was wise and powerful. All the animals obeyed him, but the king had one worry.

259

KING LEOPARD: Whom shall I name to rule after me when I die? I must find out who is the cleverest beast in our jungle land.

I will have a great feast. The drums will carry word of it throughout the jungle.

OLD TANKO: All the animals came to the king's feast. There were good things to eat and drink. The drums beat loudly, and the guests danced for three days. (*The animals dance together.*)

At last the king called them all together and spoke in a loud voice.

KING LEOPARD: Listen closely to my words, friends! Someday I will die. Someday another king or queen must rule in my place. I will choose this ruler from among you now.

FROG (*in a low whisper*): How will the king choose? If he picks the largest animal, I will have no chance at all.

RABBIT (*baring her teeth*): Perhaps he will choose the quickest. Then I shall wear the crown.

JACKAL (*holding his head up high while he pats his fur*): Surely the king has noticed how lovely my fur is. Indeed I would look the most kingly.

KING LEOPARD: Quiet, friends! I shall seek the *cleverest* among you, for your king or queen must be wise. He or she shall share all my riches and become your leader when I die.

ELEPHANT (*swaying from side to side*): Although I am very modest, O King, I must confess I am the most clever.

261

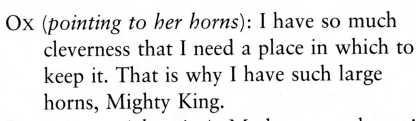

OX (*pointing to her horns*): I have so much cleverness that I need a place in which to keep it. That is why I have such large horns, Mighty King.

RHINOCEROS (*shouting*): My horns are larger! My horns are larger! (*She stamps her feet.*)

KING LEOPARD: Look at this, my people! I will throw my spear into the air. Watch! (*He throws the spear.*)

Now, listen closely. With this spear will I test you. The animal who would be your leader must throw the spear toward the sky. He or she must send it high and count to ten before it drops down to earth again.

OLD TANKO: The animals began to talk among themselves. Surely this would not be a hard thing to do, they thought.

KING LEOPARD: Each of you may come forward and sing or dance. Then you may try your skill at throwing the spear.

OLD TANKO: First to try was the elephant.

ELEPHANT (*pushing all the other animals out of his way*): I must be first. This task is too easy. Almost any one of us can do it. (*He does an awkward dance. Then he raises his trunk like a trumpet and sings. At last he throws the spear into the air.*) One! Two! Three!

OLD TANKO: The huge beast began to count, but he spoke slowly, as he did everything else. An elephant cannot easily hurry, you know.

Before he had said "Four!" the king's spear had dropped to the earth. The proud beast hung his head low, and his trunk dragged on the ground. He knew he had failed.

Next came the ox. Her wide gray horns swept the other beasts to the side.

OX (*patting her horns*): I'll throw the spear up to the sun! (*She sings while she dances. Then she tosses the spear far above her horns.*) One! Two! Three! Four!

OLD TANKO: She counted more quickly than the elephant, but she was slow, too. Before she could say "Five!" the spear was down on the ground. Off she went, ashamed.

    The chimpanzee was third.

CHIMPANZEE (*beating his chest with his two fists*): Oh, how much I would like to be king! (*He holds the spear in one arm and throws it up toward the sky.*) One-two-three-four-five-six-seven!

OLD TANKO: The other animals held their breaths. Surely, with such a quick tongue, the chimpanzee would make the count.

    But he did not. He had not even said "Eight!" before he caught the spear in his hand.

CHIMPANZEE (*running away on all fours*): Oh, how much I would like to be a turtle and pull back into my shell.

OLD TANKO: One by one, the other animals tried to count to ten while the spear was still up in the air. One by one, they all failed.

KING LEOPARD: It seems I must look somewhere else for a clever beast to rule when I am gone.

OLD TANKO: Then out from the crowd stepped an antelope.

Next to the elephant, the ox, and even the chimpanzee, the young antelope seemed small and weak. But the antelope spoke bravely.

ANTELOPE: Let me try to throw your spear, O King. (*The other animals laugh.*)

RHINOCEROS: This weak creature thinks she can do what we could not. Ho! Ho!

JACKAL: How could she fling the spear high enough to say more than two or three words? How could she ever count to ten?

OLD TANKO: But the antelope would not be turned aside.

ANTELOPE: I wish to try.

KING LEOPARD: I have promised a fair trial to all who wished to take part in this contest. Who can say what any creature can do until he or she has tried? The antelope may throw the spear.

OLD TANKO: So the other beasts were moved back to give her room. (*The antelope does a graceful dance.*)

When the antelope danced, all could see that her steps were more graceful than any other animal's. Then the antelope threw the spear far up into the air. Before it could fall to earth, the clever beast called out two words.

ANTELOPE: Five! Ten! I have counted to ten. King Leopard did not say how the count should be made.

KING LEOPARD (*laughing*): No, I did not say how the count was to be made. And as everyone knows, one can count by fives as well as by ones. The antelope has won the contest. She has proved she is the cleverest of you all. She shall be your leader when I am gone.

OLD TANKO: The other animals stared stupidly at the winner. They did not understand what had happened, but they could see that the antelope had outwitted the king.

At the feast that King Leopard gave, they all cheered for the antelope.

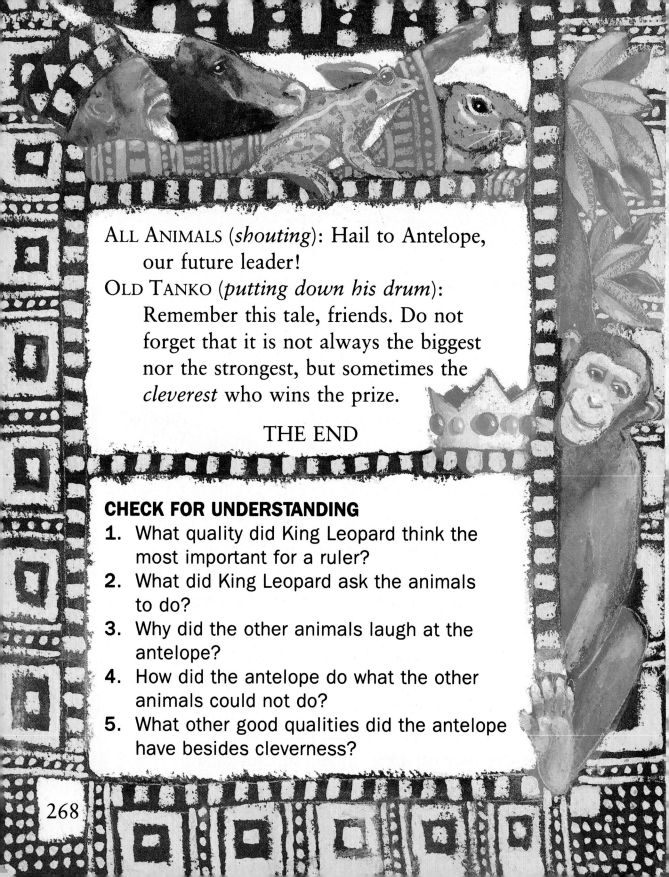

ALL ANIMALS (*shouting*): Hail to Antelope, our future leader!

OLD TANKO (*putting down his drum*): Remember this tale, friends. Do not forget that it is not always the biggest nor the strongest, but sometimes the *cleverest* who wins the prize.

THE END

CHECK FOR UNDERSTANDING

1. What quality did King Leopard think the most important for a ruler?
2. What did King Leopard ask the animals to do?
3. Why did the other animals laugh at the antelope?
4. How did the antelope do what the other animals could not do?
5. What other good qualities did the antelope have besides cleverness?

Count on Your Fingers African Style

by CLAUDIA ZASLAVSKY

How would you shop in stores where people speak another language? In an East African market, people who speak different languages come to buy and sell. To shop, they count on their fingers—African style.

What are two different ways of counting *three* on your fingers? How did the Mende people get their word for *twenty*?

You are in a faraway land. You are in East Africa. Today is market day. People come from near and far to buy all sorts of things—food, cloth, pots, beads. Market day is a great event. People meet friends they have not seen for many days. Some tell funny stories. Others have sad news to give their friends. People speak in excited voices as they buy and sell. Everyone tries to get the best price. Some people are waving their fingers as they talk.

269

You join the crowd. An orange would taste good on a hot day like this. You decide to buy three, so you can keep two for later. But how can you say that you want three oranges? You speak only English. You don't hear anyone speaking English.

What can you do? You can use your fingers. You can point to the oranges and show three on your fingers. But how will you do it? This way . . .

or this way . . . ?

Go to the orange seller and see what happens.

It works! She gives you three oranges. Now she asks you for *itatu* cents—one penny for each orange. This is how Kamba people show three on their fingers.

Three Masai boys are looking at the oranges. They talk to one another and laugh. One boy shows this sign with his right hand. How many oranges does he want? The market woman gives him three oranges, too.

The Kamba people and the Masai people live near each other in a country called Kenya. The Masai buy things like pots and knives from the Kamba. The Kamba buy cows and beads from the Masai. But they speak different languages. They can say how many they want and how much money to pay with finger counting.

Now you see some ripe yellow bananas. The Kamba farmer picked them just this morning. How can you show that you want eight bananas?

This way . . .   or this way . . .

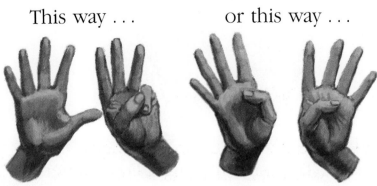

or some other way?

This is the Kamba sign for eight. The right hand holds three fingers of the left hand. Five fingers on the right and three fingers on the left make eight. The Kamba word for eight is *nyaanya*.

The Taita people also live in Kenya. The Taita sign for three is just like the Kamba sign. The Taita word is almost the same. It is *idadu*. The Kamba word is *itatu*.

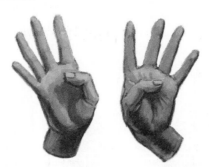

This is the Taita sign for eight. Four fingers and four fingers make eight. The Taita word for eight is *munani*. It means four and four.

What beautiful beads! The Masai women make these colorful necklaces while the men and boys take care of the cattle.

The man wants you to buy one. How many shillings does he ask for it? He waves four fingers of his right hand. What can he mean?

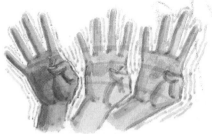

Eight shillings is the price of the beads. Why does he wave four fingers? Perhaps to show that four and four make eight.

All these people live in the same country in East Africa. They all live in Kenya. Yet they all have different ways of showing eight on their fingers.

Very small children in Africa play finger games and learn to count on their fingers. They bend the fingers of the left hand with the right thumb as they say: "This is little finger. This is the big brother of little finger. This is long finger. This one picks up the food. This is the bent thumb."

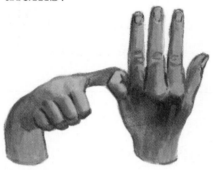

All over the world children and grown-ups sometimes use their fingers for counting. Fatu can show you her way.

Fatu lives in Sierra Leone, a country in West Africa. Often she helps her mother sell bright red tomatoes. Fatu has twenty tomatoes in her basin. Her mother laid them down as Fatu counted them on her fingers. That way she knew just how many she had.

This is how Fatu counted the tomatoes. She bent one finger for each tomato. First she bent the fingers of her left hand, starting with the little finger. Then she counted from six to ten on her right hand, starting with the little finger. For eleven to twenty, she did the same thing all over again.

Some of Fatu's people count from eleven to twenty on their toes. Her people, the Mende, have a special word for twenty. It is *nu gboyongo*. It means a whole person. All ten fingers and all ten toes have been counted.

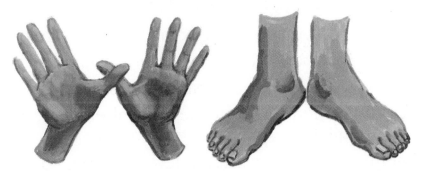

Fatu's mother does not need to count on her fingers. She can do even the biggest sums in her head. Fatu will be able to do that, too, when she is older.

Do you know that some of our English number words are named for finger counting? *Eleven* means one left. Count out all ten fingers. Then you will need one more to reach eleven. *Twelve* means two left over, after counting all ten fingers.

Many people in South Africa show six by holding up the right thumb. The Zulu people live in South Africa. *Isithipa* is the Zulu word for six. It means take the thumb.

Isishiyagalombili means leave out two fingers. Can you guess what number that is?

Isishiyagalombili is the Zulu word for eight. The word tells how many fingers are not used. People all over the world count on their fingers. Their number names prove it!

Can you make up your own finger signs for the numbers from one to ten? Ask your friends to guess which numbers you are showing. Then make up new number names to go with your signs.

CHECK FOR UNDERSTANDING

1. What do the Kamba and Masai people buy from each other?
2. What are two different ways of counting *three* on your fingers?
3. What two tribes have almost the same word for *eight*?
4. What are two ways the people of Sierra Leone count to twenty?
5. How did the Mende people get their word for *twenty*?

FINGER MULTIPLICATION

by LINDA OLSEN GEORGE

Most children begin learning to count on their fingers. You may have done simple adding and subtracting on yours, but did you know that you can use your fingers to multiply?

How should you hold your hands to multiply numbers greater than five? Do you have to know left from right to do finger multiplication?

Fingers are useful in math. We all know that. Remember when you were first learning how to count, to add, and to subtract? During that time you probably used your fingers often. But once you learned the basic addition facts, you stopped using your fingers as tools.

Now you can use your fingers to check your multiplication. Are you not sure of yourself when you multiply 6s, 7s, 8s, and 9s? There's no easy substitute for memorizing the multiplication facts, but you can still count on your fingers when you need to check an answer—or just for fun!

277

EASY NINES

Multiplying by 9 is a good way to start. First, hold up your hands and give each finger a number like this:

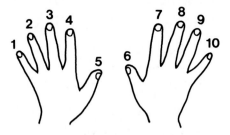

(If you have a hard time remembering which finger is which, you can write the numbers on your fingernails with a pencil.)

Now let's try a basic multiplication problem using 9 as a factor:

$$9 \times 3 = \underline{\quad}$$

Since 3 is the other factor, bend your third finger down like this:

Count the fingers to the left of the bent finger to get the ten's value—2 fingers, or 20, in this case. Then count the number of fingers to the right of the bent finger to get the one's value—7 fingers or 7 ones. Thus, 9×3 equals $20 + 7$, or 27.

Just to be sure you understand what to do, try another problem:

$$9 \times 7 = \underline{\quad}$$

Your fingers should look like this:

And the steps are:
1. Hands up.
2. Bend finger number 7.
3. Number of fingers to the left: 6.
4. Number of fingers to the right: 3.
5. So 9 × 7 equals 60 + 3, or 63.

Does this answer agree with yours?

Try doing this to multiply 9 with the other numbers from 1 to 10. Do the answers agree with the facts you've learned in math?

A CHALLENGE

Now that your fingers have been well exercised and your mind is ready, let's move into a harder area of finger multiplication—to all the basic facts greater than 5. This time place your hands in front of you with your thumbs up and your palms facing you. Using this position, give numbers to your fingers, as shown:

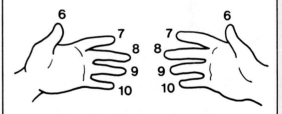

Now pick any multiplication combination with factors greater than 5. How about this problem?

7 × 8 = ___

First, close all fingers below fingers 7 and 8.

Then:

1. Add the open fingers on both hands to give you the ten's value. There are 2 + 3, or 5, fingers open, so we have 5 tens, or 50, so far.

2. Multiply the number of closed fingers on one hand by the number of closed fingers on the other hand. This is the unit's (or one's) value. There are 3 fingers closed on one hand and 2 fingers closed on the other hand. This gives 3 × 2, or 6, as the unit's value.

3. Last, add what you got in the first two steps. The answer is 56 (50 + 6).

So 7 × 8 = 56, based on finger multiplication. Is this correct? Certainly it is!

Some problems, like 6 × 7, are a little harder, but do work if you follow all the steps. Let's try it:

6 × 7 = ___

Remember to close all fingers below fingers number 6 and 7. Your hands should look like this:

280

Now:

1. Add the number of open fingers on both hands to get the ten's value: 3 open fingers represents 30.
2. Multiply the number of closed fingers on each hand for the unit's value: 4 fingers on one hand and 3 fingers on the other hand— $4 \times 3 = 12$.
3. Now add 30 and 12 to get 42. Our fingers gave us the right answer again!

Remember that while finger multiplication is fun to do, it's not a substitute for memorizing the multiplication facts. Nothing is as good as brain power, but fingers are something you can count on if all else fails.

CHECK FOR UNDERSTANDING

1. Do you have to know your left from your right to do finger multiplication? Explain your answer.
2. When you use your fingers to multiply by nine, from which direction do you begin counting?
3. Think about the answers you get when you multiply by nine: 18, 27, 36, 45, 54, 63, 72, 81. What is alike about all of these numbers?
4. How should you hold your hands to multiply numbers greater than five?

The Legend of the Bluebonnet

by TOMIE dePAOLA

In this legend, the Comanche people have had no rain for a very long time, so they are suffering greatly. They seek a way to change things, but what they learn is that someone must make a sacrifice.

How did the Comanche's shaman explain the drought? What did he say would end the drought?

"Great Spirits, the land is dying. Your People are dying, too," the long line of dancers sang. "Tell us what we have done to anger you. End this drought. Save your People. Tell us what we must do so you will send the rain that will bring back life."

For three days, the dancers danced to the sound of the drums. And for three days, the

People called Comanche watched and waited.
Even though the hard winter was over, no
healing rains came.

Drought and famine are hardest on the
very young and the very old. Among the few
children left was a small girl named
She-Who-Is-Alone. She sat by herself watching
the dancers. In her lap was a doll made from
buckskin. It was a warrior doll. The eyes,
nose, and mouth were painted on with the
juice of berries. It wore beaded leggings and a
belt of polished bone. On its head were
brilliant blue feathers from the bird who cries
"Jay-jay-jay." She loved her doll very much.

"Soon," She-Who-Is-Alone said to her doll, "the shaman will go off alone to the top of the hill to listen for the words of the Great Spirits. Then, we will know what to do so that once more the rains will come. The Earth will be green and alive and the People will be rich again."

As she talked, she thought of the mother who made the doll. She thought of the father who brought the blue feathers. She thought of the grandfather and the grandmother she had never known. They were all like shadows. It seemed long ago that they had died from the famine. The People had named her and cared for her. The warrior doll was the only thing she had left from those distant days.

"The sun is setting," the runner called as he ran through the camp. "The shaman is returning."

The People gathered in a circle and the shaman spoke.

"I have heard the words of the Great Spirits," he said. "The People have become selfish. For years, they have taken from the Earth without giving anything back. The Great Spirits say the People must sacrifice. We must make a burnt offering of the most valued possession among us. The ashes of this offering shall then be scattered to the four points of the Earth, the Home of the Winds. When this sacrifice is made, drought and famine will cease. Life will be restored to the Earth and to the People!"

The People sang a song of thanks to the Great Spirits for telling them what they must do.

285

"I'm sure it is not my new bow that the Great Spirits want," a warrior said.

"Or my special blanket," a woman added. Everyone went to the tepees to talk and think over what the Great Spirits had asked. Everyone, that is, except She-Who-Is-Alone. She held her doll tightly to her heart.

"You," she said, looking at the doll. "You are my most valued possession. It is you the Great Spirits want." She knew what she must do.

As the council fires died out and the tepee flaps began to close, the small girl returned to the tepee, where she slept, to wait. The night outside was still except for the distant sound of the night bird with the red wings. Soon everyone in the tepee was asleep, except She-Who-Is-Alone.

Under the ashes of the tepee fire, one stick still glowed. She took it and quietly crept out into the night. She ran to the place on the hill where the Great Spirits had spoken to the shaman. Stars filled the sky. There was no moon.

"O Great Spirits," She-Who-Is-Alone said, "here is my warrior doll. It is the only thing I have from my family who died in this famine. It is my most valued possession. Please accept it."

Then, gathering twigs, she started a fire with the glowing firestick. The small girl watched as the twigs began to catch and burn. She thought of her grandmother and grandfather, her mother and father, and all the People—their suffering, their hunger. Before she could change her mind, she thrust the doll into the fire.

She watched until the flames died down and the ashes had grown cold. Then, scooping up a handful, She-Who-Is-Alone scattered the ashes to the Home of the Winds, the North and the East, the South and the West. And there she fell asleep until the first light of the morning sun woke her.

She looked out over the hill. Stretching out from all sides, where the ashes had fallen, the ground was covered with flowers— beautiful flowers, as blue as the feathers in the hair of the doll, as blue as the feathers of the bird who cries "Jay-jay-jay."

287

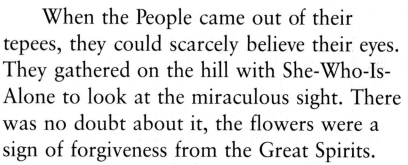

When the People came out of their
tepees, they could scarcely believe their eyes.
They gathered on the hill with She-Who-Is-
Alone to look at the miraculous sight. There
was no doubt about it, the flowers were a
sign of forgiveness from the Great Spirits.

As the People sang and danced their
thanks to the Great Spirits, a warm rain
began to fall. The land began to live again.
From that day on, the little girl was known
by another name—"One-Who-Dearly-Loved-
Her-People."

Every spring, the Great Spirits remember
the sacrifice of a little girl. They fill the hills
and valleys of the land, now called Texas,
with the beautiful blue flowers.

Even to this very day.

CHECK FOR UNDERSTANDING

1. How did the shaman explain the drought?
2. What did he say would end it?
3. In what way was She-Who-Is-Alone different from others of the Comanche people?
4. What did the people regard as a sign of forgiveness from the Great Spirit?
5. A legend is a story handed down from the past. Some legends are thought to be partly true. What are four things from this legend that you think could be true?

WRITE ABOUT

"The Legend of the Bluebonnet"

In the story, the girl's name is changed from She-Who-Is-Alone to One-Who-Dearly-Loved-Her-People. These are names that tell about the little girl. They describe important things about her. Think of two people you know well. Give them names like the Comanche people used. Explain why you gave each person the name you did.

289

LITERATURE

Similes

A story uses words to say things that would be much easier to see in a picture. An artist can show the shape and color of clouds with lines and paint. The artist can also make it clear that the clouds are storm clouds.

The writer of a story must find a way to paint for the reader the same picture in words. One of the ways writers do this is by using similes. A **simile** compares one thing to another by using the words like or as. The writer might say, for example, that the clouds were "like huge gray waves rolling across the sky." The writer might say that the clouds were moving "as fast as a rushing freight train."

The writer used similes to compare the clouds to two other things. To give an idea of the size and shape of the clouds, the writer compared them to huge waves. To give an idea of the movement of the clouds, the writer compared them to a rushing freight train.

What is another reason the writer chose these things to compare the clouds to? What other quality about the clouds is shown by comparing them to huge waves and a rushing train? Do these similes give you a sense of safety or danger? They probably give you a sense of danger, a feeling close to what you feel when a storm is coming.

See if you can find the simile in the paragraph from "The Legend of the Bluebonnet" below. Then ask yourself what two things are being compared. Why did the writer choose this simile? How does it help tell you more about the way the girl feels?

As she talked, she thought of the mother who made the doll. She thought of the father who brought the blue feathers. She thought of the grandfather and the grandmother she had never known. They were all like shadows. It seemed long ago that they had died from the famine.

The simile in the paragraph is ". . . like shadows." The simile helps show the girl's feelings. It shows that the girl felt her family members were no longer clear memories. Instead, they were more like ghosts, dark outlines without clear features.

A simile is a good way to create a picture, mood, or feeling because it can suggest a lot in a few words. Reread the paragraph from "The Legend of the Bluebonnet." This time leave out the sentence with the simile. Without the simile, you don't get much idea of the way the girl felt about her family lost in the famine.

Just·A·Taste

Maurice's Room

by PAULA FOX

Your mother wants everything—
everything!—off the floor of your room. You
certainly don't want to throw anything away,
but there's no drawer or shelf space left for
anything. That's exactly what Maurice's
problem is. What would you do if you were
Maurice?

How large is Maurice's room? Why do you
think Mr. Klenk is so helpful to Maurice?

Everything Off the Floor!

Maurice's room measured six long steps
in one direction and five in the other. The
distance from the floor to the ceiling was
three times higher than Maurice. There was
one window through which Maurice could
see several other windows as well as a piece
of the sky. From the middle of the ceiling
dangled a long string. It was the kind used to
tie up packages of laundry. Attached to the
end of the string was a dried octopus. It was
the newest addition to Maurice's collection.
When his mother or father walked into his
room—which wasn't often—the octopus
swung back and forth a little in the breeze.

Maurice had used a ladder to climb up high enough to tack the string to the ceiling. The ladder was still leaning against the wall. Instead of returning it to Mr. Klenk, the janitor of his building, from whom he had borrowed it, Maurice was using the steps for shelves. Even though Maurice's father, Mr. Henry, had put up a dozen shelves around the room for all of Maurice's things, there still weren't enough.

Maurice knew how to walk around his room without stepping on anything. So did his friend Jacob. But no one else did.

As his mother and father often said to visitors, it was astonishing how much junk a person could find in one city block. His mother said Maurice kept their block clean because he brought up everything from the street to his room. His father said Maurice should get a salary from the Department of Sanitation because of all the work he was doing in cleaning up the city. At least once a month Mr. and Mrs. Henry talked about moving to the country. It would be better for Maurice, they said. But then they would decide to wait a little longer.

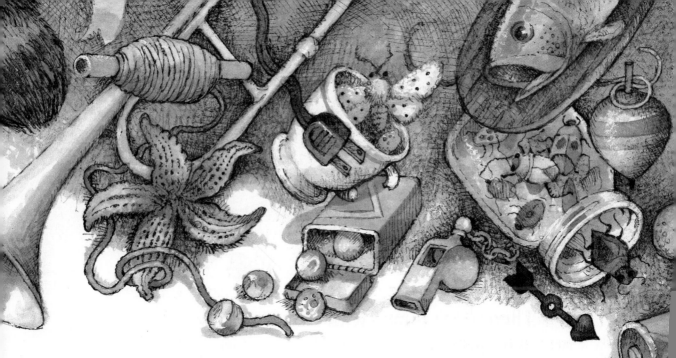

Some visitors said that collections like Maurice's showed that a child would become a great scientist. Many great scientists had collected junk when they were eight years old. Other visitors said Maurice would outgrow his collection and become interested in other things. Some suggested to the Henrys that they should buy Maurice a dog. Or send him to music school so that his time might be spent more usefully.

In his room Maurice had a bottle of dead beetles, white moths in a cup without a handle, a squirrel hide tacked to a board, a snakeskin on a wire hanger, a raccoon tail, a glass of shrimp eggs, a plate of worms, a box of turtle food.

There were things with which to make
other things. There were nails of different
sizes, screws, wire, butterfly bolts, scraps of
wood, sockets, filaments from electric light
bulbs, cardboard from grocery boxes, two
orange crates, a handsaw, and a hammer. On
the top of a chest of drawers, Maurice kept
stones and pebbles, dried tar balls, fragments
of brick, pieces of colored bottle glass that
had been worn smooth, and gray rocks that
glistened with mica.

On his window sill there was a heap of
dried moss next to a turtle bowl. In the bowl
lived several salamanders, half hidden by mud
and wet grass. On the same sill he kept some
plants from the five-and-ten cent store. They
looked dead. Now and then a cactus would
put out a new shoot.

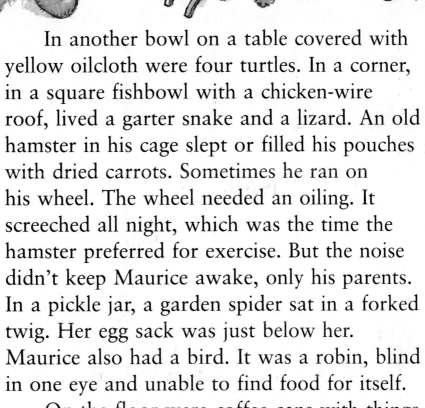

In another bowl on a table covered with
yellow oilcloth were four turtles. In a corner,
in a square fishbowl with a chicken-wire
roof, lived a garter snake and a lizard. An old
hamster in his cage slept or filled his pouches
with dried carrots. Sometimes he ran on
his wheel. The wheel needed an oiling. It
screeched all night, which was the time the
hamster preferred for exercise. But the noise
didn't keep Maurice awake, only his parents.
In a pickle jar, a garden spider sat in a forked
twig. Her egg sack was just below her.
Maurice also had a bird. It was a robin, blind
in one eye and unable to find food for itself.

On the floor were coffee cans with things
in them: an eggbeater with a missing gear, a
pile of dead starfish, cigar boxes, clockworks,
hinges, and a very large grater with sharp
dents on all four sides. The grater was orange
with rust. It stood in the middle of the room
beneath the octopus. You would have to use
a magnifying glass to see all the other things
Maurice had found.

His bed had two blankets and a pillow without a pillowcase. Sometimes a small goose feather pricked its way through the ticking, and Maurice would put it away in an envelope. He had used two pillowcases for his collecting expeditions. After that his mother wouldn't give him any more.

There was one tidy corner in Maurice's room. It was where he had pushed his Christmas toys. They were a month old now, and the dust covered them evenly. They were like furniture or bathroom fixtures. Maurice felt there wasn't much to be done with them.

It was the end of January, and Maurice had just come home from school. He put his books on his bed and went to see what the snake was doing. It was lying on its rock. The lizard was watching it. The robin was so still it looked stuffed. But it cocked its head when Maurice whistled at it. The hamster was hiding bits of carrot in the sawdust at the bottom of its cage. The salamanders had buried themselves in the mud. Maurice was arranging little piles of food for his animals when he heard his uncle's voice from down the hall.

"Lily," his uncle was saying to his mother, "you should dynamite that room!"

"There must be another way," his mother said.

"You'd better give it up," said his uncle. "Maurice will never clean it."

"If we lived in the country, it would be different," said his mother.

"Perhaps," said his uncle.

Maurice took two walnuts from his pocket and cracked them together. His mother came to the door.

"Get everything off the floor," she said in a low, even voice as though she were counting moving freight cars.

"Where will I put things?" asked Maurice.

"I don't care," she said, "But clean the floor! Or else I'll bring in the broom, the dustpan, and a very large box. And that will be that!"

The doorbell rang. It was Jacob.

"Jacob can help you," his mother said.

Jacob was seven, but he looked bigger than Maurice. It was because he was wearing so many clothes—scarves, mittens, sweaters, two hats, and several pairs of socks. He began to take off his outer clothing, laying each item in a pile at his feet. Meanwhile Maurice explained the predicament.

"What are we going to do?" asked Jacob.

Maurice looked at the chest of drawers. The pebbles and rocks had been moved to the floor, and the chest was now covered with oatmeal boxes. He looked at the table. He could barely see the yellow oilcloth. It was hidden by sections of a witch doctor's mask he and Jacob had begun to make the week before. The turtles had been moved next to the salamanders on the window sill.

"There are five more floors in this room if you count the walls and ceiling," Maurice said to Jacob. Jacob looked smaller and thinner now that he was down to his shirt and pants.

"I see," said Jacob.

"We'll have to ask Mr. Klenk to help us," said Maurice.

Jacob began to sort out nails. Then he stopped. "But we won't be able to do that with everything! And how can we get it all done in just a day?"

"Mr. Klenk will know," said Maurice.

Mr. Klenk, the janitor, lived in the basement five floors down. The basement smelled like wet mops, damp cement, pipes, and old furniture stuffing. But it was clean. Mr. Klenk had told Maurice that he couldn't relax a second or he would be drowned by the rubbish that poured out of all the apartments.

"Overwhelming!" Mr. Klenk often exclaimed. "It's a race between me and the junk," he would say. "If I let it get an edge on me, I'll get shoved right out of the city." But Mr. Klenk didn't seem to feel the same way about Maurice's collection.

"Well, you're selective, my boy," he had said once. "Besides, I think you've got something in mind for all that stuff of yours."

The two boys rang the janitor's bell. Mr. Klenk opened his door.

"I have to get everything off the floor," Maurice said. "Could you help us a little?"

"What do you have in mind?"

"There's plenty of space on the walls," said Maurice.

Mr. Klenk nodded. "I know," he said. "But you didn't bring back my ladder, did you?"

"He forgot," said Jacob timidly. Mr. Klenk peered at him. Jacob backed away.

"Can you come now?" asked Maurice.

"Let's go," answered Mr. Klenk.

When they reached Maurice's room, Mr. Klenk stopped at the doorway.

"How am I suppose to get in there?" he asked.

Jacob cleared a path for him. Maurice took all the things off the ladder steps. In a few minutes Mr. Klenk was at work.

First Maurice chose a starfish. He handed it to Jacob, who held it up to Mr. Klenk on the ladder. Next came the rusty grater. In an hour everything was hanging either from the ceiling or from the walls. The animals paid no attention to the fact that they were suspended above the floor. The hamster went to sleep. His cage swung gently like a hammock in a light breeze.

By six o'clock they could see the floor boards. It was a good floor, and Maurice and Jacob sat down on it.

"Now we have room for more things," said Maurice.

Maurice's mother and his uncle came to the door.

"Wow!" said Uncle.

Mrs. Henry looked pale. "I didn't have *that* in mind," she said.

"Well, Lily, they've cleared the floor," said the uncle.

After Maurice's uncle and Mrs. Henry went back to the kitchen, Mr. Klenk picked up his ladder and started to leave. Then he seemed to remember something. He tapped Maurice on the shoulder.

"Would you like a stuffed bear?" he asked.

"I'd like a bear," Maurice said.

"A tenant left it when he moved out," said Mr. Klenk. "Send your man down for it in the near future." He nodded at Jacob.

Does it seem as though Maurice's problems might be starting all over again with the stuffed bear? Do you think Maurice's family might move to the country, as his mother suggested at one point? Read the book Maurice's Room *by Paula Fox to find out what happens to Maurice and his very unusual collections.*

CHECK FOR UNDERSTANDING

1. How large is Maurice's room?
2. What did Maurice have that belonged to Mr. Klenk, the janitor?
3. Why did Mr. Henry say Maurice should get a salary from the Department of Sanitation?
4. Was Maurice's mother pleased with the way he cleared off his floor? Give reasons for your answer.
5. Why do you think Mr. Klenk was so helpful to Maurice?

THINK ABOUT IT

Think about the characters in the stories you have read. How do the characters solve their predicaments or puzzles?

- What should the ox have done sooner than it did?
- How did thinking about the broken glass in a different way help Encyclopedia Brown?
- How did thinking about King Leopard's test in a different way help the antelope?
- How do the people of East, West, and South Africa buy things from one another if they all speak different languages?
- How did thinking about the warrior doll in a different way help She-Who-Is-Alone?
- What would have happened if Maurice hadn't been able to solve his problem?

After reading and thinking about these different stories, which ones do you think are about predicaments? Which ones are about puzzles?

WRITE ABOUT IT

Imagine that you are Maurice. Write a paragraph telling how you might have solved the predicament in a different way. What would you have done if you were Maurice, and you didn't think of hanging everything from the ceiling?

READ ABOUT IT

Belinda's Hurricane by Elizabeth Winthrop. E. P. Dutton & Co., Inc., 1984. During a storm, Belinda has a chance to strike out on her own to help solve a mystery.

The Celery Stalks at Midnight by James Howe. Atheneum Publishers, 1984. Chester, the cat, is sure that Bunnicula, the rabbit, is a vampire. He races around trying to save everybody that he can.

Encyclopedia Brown and the Case of the Mysterious Handprints by Donald Sobol. William Morrow & Co., Inc., 1985. Leroy Brown, Idaville's young detective, finds interesting clues to help him solve ten new cases.

Julia's Magic by Eleanor Cameron. E. P. Dutton & Co., Inc., 1984. A broken bottle, the threat of losing their home, and a case of poison oak cause a crisis within the Redfern family. The adults frown at Julia's tries to help until she asks, "Didn't any of you ever do anything awful when you were kids?"

GLOSSARY

A

ab·surd (ab surd′) *adj.* against good sense.

al·bum (al′ bəm) *n.* a book in which to keep or hold things, such as stamps.

al·though (ôl <u>th</u>ō′) *conj.* even though.

an·ces·tor (an′ ses′ tər) *n. pl.*, **an·ces·tors.** a person from whom one is descended; a parent from one's family long ago.

an·guish (ang′ gwish) *n.* a feeling of great sadness and fear.

an·nounce (ə nouns′) *v.*, **an·nounced.** to make known.

an·te·lope (ant′ əl ōp′) *n.* a graceful animal that looks like a goat.

as·par·a·gus (əs par′ ə gəs) *n.* a plant with green or white spears that are eaten as a vegetable.

as·ton·ish (əs ton′ ish) *v.*, **as·ton·ished.** to surprise greatly.

av·er·age (av′ rij) *adj.* that most often found; usual.

awk·ward (ôk′ wərd) *adj.* without skill; clumsy.

B

bal·le·ri·na (bal′ ə rē′ nə) *n.* a woman ballet dancer.

ba·sin (bā′ sin) *n.* a bowl.

ben·zine (ben′ zēn) *n.* a liquid made from oil, which may be used for cleaning and fuel.

bril·liant (bril′ yənt) *adj.* shining; bright.

buck·skin (buck′skin′) *n.* the skin or hide of a deer.

budge (buj) *v.*, **budged.** to move a little bit.

bur·row (bur′ō) *v.* to dig into.

C

car·i·bou (kar′ ə bōō′) *n. pl.* large deer that live in the far North.

carve (kärv) *v.* to shape a figure out of wood or some material by cutting into the material.

carv·ing (kär′ ving) *n. pl.*, **carv·ings.** something cut or carved out of wood.

cast (kast) *v.* to throw.

cau·tious (kô′ shəs) *adj.* careful.—**cau′ tious·ly,** *adv.*

cease (sēs) *v.* to end.

cel·e·brate (sel′ ə brāt′) *v.* to do something special because of a happening.

cer·e·mo·ny (ser′ ə mō′nē) *n.* a way of doing something to mark a special time.

chair·per·son (cher′ pur′ sən) *n.* the person who takes charge of group meetings.

char·i·ot (char′ ē ət) *n.* a wagon with two wheels, pulled by horses.

clam·or (klam′ ər) *n.* loud noise.

cli·mate (klī′ mit) *n.* the weather most often found in a place; the usual weather.

clus·ter (klus′ tər) *n.* things put or grouped together; a bunch.

coax (kōks) *v.* to try to get someone to do something.

col·lapse (kə laps′) *v.,* **col·laps·ing.** to break down; to lie down from being worn out.

com·bi·na·tion (kom′ bə nā′- shən) *n.* a mix; a joining together.

com·mand (kə mand′) *v.,* **com·mand·ed.** to order.

com·mo·tion (kə mō′ shən) *n.* an upsetting state of things; mixed up state.

con·vince (kən vins′) *v.,* **con·vinced.** to make someone believe.

coon·skin (kōōn′ skin′) *adj.* skin of a raccoon.

coun·cil (koun′ səl) *n.* a group of people called upon to make laws or to give advice.

co·zy (kō′ zē) *adj.,* comfortable; snug.

crouch (krouch) *v.,* **crouched.** to bend one's knees in order to lower one's body; to stoop.

cube (kyōōb) *n. pl.,* **cubes.** a block, usually with six square sides.

D

dain·ty (dān′ tē) *adj.* fussy; picky.—**dain′ ti·ly,** *adv.*

deer·stalk·er (dēr′ stok′ ər) *n.,* a person who hunts deer.— *adj.* used or worn in hunting deer: *A deerstalker's cap has earmuffs.*

de·spair (di sper′) *v.* to give up all hope.

de·stroy (di stroi′) *v.* to do away with; to get rid of.

PRONUNCIATION KEY
at; āpe; cär; end; mē; it; īce; hot; ōld; fôrk; wood; fōol; oil; out; up; turn; sing; thin; this, hw in white; zh in treasure; ə stands for a in ago, e in taken, i in pencil, o in lemon, u in circus.

di·am·e·ter (dī am′ ə tər) *n.* the length of a line through the center of a circle.

din·ner·time (din ər′ tīm′) *n.* the time when dinner is often eaten.

din·o·saur (dī′nə sôr′) *n.* a huge animal that lived long ago and is no longer living.

dis·cour·age (dis kur′ ij) *v.*, **dis·cour·aged.** to take away hope; to make tired of trying.

dis·turb (dis turb′) *v.*, **dis·turb·ing.** to upset.

drought (drout) *n.* a long time without rain.

E _____

em·bar·rass (em bar′ əs) *v.*, **em·bar·rassed.** to make someone feel foolish.

en·trance (en′ trəns) *n.* opening to a place; door.

es·pe·cial·ly (es pesh′ ə lē) *adv.* most of all.

ex·hib·it (eg zib′ it) *n. pl.*, **ex·hib·its.** things to be seen at a show.

ex·pe·di·tion (eks′ pə dish′ ən) *n. pl.* **ex·pe·di·tions.** a trip made for a special reason.

F _____

fac·tor (fak′ tər) *n.* any of the numbers which when multiplied together form a product; anything that helps bring about an end.

fa·mil·iar (fə mil′ yər) *adj.* known.

fam·ine (fam′ in) *n.* a long time with very little food.

fault (fôlt) *n.* something done wrongly.

fierce (fērs) *adj.* wild.

fil·a·ment (fil′ ə mənt) *n. pl.*, **fil·a·ments.** a wire from a light bulb; a fine thread.

fix·ture (fiks′ chər) *n. pl.*, **fix·tures.** something that is fixed or built in a room such as a sink in the kitchen.

frag·ment (frag′ mənt) *n. pl.*, **frag·ments.** a bit or piece.

fringe (frinj) *n. pl.*, **fringes.** trimming of fur, string, or the like.

fur·ther·more (fur′ thər môr′) *adv.* besides.

fu·ture (fyo͞o′ chər) *adj.* in time to come.

G _____

gen·tian (jen′ shən) *n. pl.*, **gen·tians.** a blue flower that may be found along wet banks.

ger·bil (jur′ bil) *n.* a mouselike animal with soft gray or brown fur which may be kept as a pet.

glint (glint) *v.* to shine.

glis·ten (glis′ ən) *v.*, **glis·tened.** to shine.

grin (grin) *v.*, **grinning.** to smile from great happiness.

H _____

hail (hāl) *n.* hooray; praise.

ham·mock (ham′ ək) *n.* a swinging cot or bed made by fastening a heavy piece of cloth to two poles.

ham·ster (ham′ stər) *n.* an animal that looks like a mouse with fat cheeks and a short tail.

harsh (härsh) *adj.* very hard; rough.

health·y (hel′ thē) *adj.* having good health.

heart·i·ly (härt′ əl ē) *adv.* with strong feeling.

hes·i·tant (hez′ ə tənt) *adj.* unsure; not certain.—
hes′ i·tant·ly, *adv.*

hes·i·tate (hez′ ə tāt′) *v.*, **hes·i·tat·ed.** to stop for a minute.

horde (hôrd) *n. pl.*, **hordes.** great numbers; bunches.

I _____

im·mense (i mens′) *adj.* huge; very big.

in·cred·i·ble (in kred′ ə bəl) *adj.* unbelievable; hard to believe.

in·sist (in sist′) *v.*, **in·sist·ed.** to speak as if one will not change his or her mind.

in·sult (in sult′) *v.*, **in·sult·ed.** to hurt the feelings of.

in·ter·rupt (in′ tə rupt′) *v.*, **in·ter·rup·ted.** to break into something that is going on.

in·ves·ti·gate (in ves′ tə gāt′) *v.* to look.

PRONUNCIATION KEY
at; āpe; cär; end; mē; it; īce; hot; ōld; fôrk; wood; fool; oil; out; up; turn; sing; thin; this, hw in white; zh in treasure; ə stands for a in ago, e in taken, i in pencil, o in lemon, u in circus.

J

jack·al (jak′ əl) *n.* a wild animal that looks something like a dog with a bushy tail and long nose.

jet·ty (jet′ ē) *n.* something built out into the water; a dock.

K

ki·mo·no (ki mō′ nə) *n.* a robe worn by Japanese men and women.

L

li·cense (lī′ səns) *n.* the right to own or do something; a permit.

lilt·ing (lilt′ ing) *adj.* cheery; happy.

lit·er·ar·y (lit′ ə rer′ ē) *adj.* having to do with written works such as stories and poems.

lit·ter (lit′ ər) *n.* baby animals born at one time.

lot (lot) *n.* a great many.

lunge (lunj) *v.* **lunged.** to move suddenly toward.

lurch (lurch) *v.*, **lurched.** to swing suddenly.

M

mag·nif·i·cent (mag nif′ ə sənt) *adj.* wonderful; splendid.

mag·ni·fy·ing glass (mag′ nə fī′ ing glas) *n.* a piece of glass that makes something look bigger.

mar·ma·lade (mär′ mə lād′) *n.* a jam made from oranges.— *adj.* having the same color as the jam made from oranges.

mas·sive (mas′ iv) *adj.* huge.

med·i·cine (med′ ə sin) *n.* materials to help the sick or the hurt get well.

mem·o·rize (mem′ ə rīz′) *v.*, **mem·o·riz·ing.** to learn by heart; to learn something so that it can be remembered and retold exactly.

men·ace (men′ is) *v.*, **men·a·cing.** to put in danger.

min·gle (ming′ gəl) *v.*, **min·gled.** to mix together.

mi·rac·u·lous (mi rak′ yə ləs) *adj.* hard to believe; amazing.

mis·take (mis tāk′) *n.* something done wrong.

moc·ca·sin (mok′ ə sin) *n. pl.*, **moc·ca·sins.** a soft shoe with no heel; slipper.

mod·est (mod′ ist) *adj.* not boastful; quiet about one's good points.

murk·y (mur′ kē) *adj.* dim; gray.

mur·mur (mur′ mər) *v.*, **mur·mured.** to make soft noises; to speak softly; to whisper.

mu·se·um (myoo zē′ əm) *n.* a place where things of interest in art, science, and history may be seen.

N _____

na·tive (nā′ tiv) *n. pl.*, **na·tives.** a person born and often still living in a place.

neat (nēt) *adj.* great; wonderful.

nec·es·sar·y (nes′ ə ser′ ē) *adj.* needed.

night·mare (nīt′ mer′) *n.* a bad dream.—**night′ mar′ ish,** *adj.*

O _____

ob·long (ob′ lông′) *adj.* longer than wide; shaped like an eye.

ob·serve (əb zurv′) *v.*, **ob·served.** to see.

ob·vi·ous (ob′ vē əs) *adj.* clear; plain to see.—**ob′ vi·ous·ly,** *adv.*

oc·cur (ə kur′) *v.*, **oc·curred.** to take place; to happen.

o·dor (ō′ dər) *n.* smell.

out·sid·er (out′ sīd′ ər) *n. pl*, **out·sid·ers.** a person who is not part of the group; one who does not belong.

out·wit (out′ wit′) *v.* **out·wit·ted.** to win by cleverness.

o·val (ō′ vəl) *adj.* shaped like an egg.

o·ver·whelm (ō′ vər hwelm′) *v.*, **o·ver·whelm·ing.** to give too much to face; to overcome.

P _____

par·tic·u·lar (pər tik′yə lər) *adj.* special.

pas·sen·ger (pas′ ən jər) *n. pl.*, **pas·sen·gers.** a rider on a bus, train, plane, or the like.

peer (pēr) *v.*, **peer·ing.** to look as if trying to find something.

per·haps (pər haps′) *adv.* maybe.

plight (plīt) *n.* a bad state of things.

pos·ses·sion (pə zesh′ ən) *n.* something one owns; something belonging to someone.

pre·dic·a·ment (pri dik′ ə mənt) *n.* a problem; trouble.

pre·fer (pri fur′) *v.,* **pre·ferred.** to like better or best.

price (prīs) *n.* what must be paid in order to buy something.

pros·per·ous (pros′ pər əs) *adj.* having good things; rich.

pry (prī) *v.,* **pry·ing.** to use something to break open or apart.

Q _____

quea·sy (kwē′ zē) *adj.* sick to one's stomach; uneasy.

R _____

rack·et (rak′ it) *n.* a loud, upsetting noise.

rec·om·mend (rek′ ə mend′) *v.* to name or tell what one thinks is best; suggest.

reg·is·ter (rej′ is tər) *v.,* **reg·is·tered.** to sign in; put on written notice.

re·late (ri lāt′) *v.* to tell what happened.

re·mark·a·ble (ri mär′kə bəl) *adj.* surprising; unusual.— **re·mark′a·bly,** *adv.*

rep·re·sent (rep′ ri zent′) *v.,* to stand for.

res·tau·rant (res′ tər ənt) *n.* a place where food is cooked and set before people at tables.

ripe (rīp) *adj.* ready to be eaten; fully grown.

S _____

sac·ri·fice (sak′ rə fīs′) *v.* to give up something of value.

sal·a·ry (sal′ ə rē) *n.* a wage; money paid for work done.

sat·is·fac·tion (sat′ is fak′ shən) *n.* in a way that pleases; a liking.

scarce·ly (skers′ lē) *adv.* almost never.

scour (skour) *v.,* **scoured.** to look over everything; to explore.

se·lec·tive (si lek′ tiv) *adj.* careful in picking and choosing.

sep·a·rate (sep′ ə rāt′) *v.* to place apart; to break up.

se·ri·ous (sēr′ ē əs) *adj.* not able to joke about a matter or most matters.

shil·ling (shil′ ing) *n. pl.*, **shil·lings.** a coin.

sit·u·a·tion (sich′ o͞o ā′ shən) *n.* a state; how things are.

ski (skē) *n. pl.*, **skis.** one of two long, turned-up wooden or metal strips worn on the feet in order to move over the snow.

skim (skim) *v.*, **skimmed.** to slide or move across.

smoth·er (smu<u>th</u>′ ər) *v.*, **smoth·ered.** to cover.

sod (sod) *n.* the top part of the ground.

sod·den (sod′ ən) *adj.* wet; soaked.

stalk (stôk) *v.*, **stalked.** to move through a place as in hunting.

stat·ue (stach′ o͞o) *n. pl.*, **stat·ues.** something made out of materials to look like a person or animal.

stead·y (sted′ ē) *adj.* without letup; at the same rate.— **stead′i·ly,** *adv.*

stock·y (stok′ ē) *adj.* strong and husky.

stor·age (stôr′ ij) *n.* where goods not in use are kept.—*adj.* for being kept while not in use.

sub·sti·tute (sub′ stə to͞ot′) *n.* something to take the place of.

sus·pend (sə spend′) *v.* **sus·pend·ed.** to hang; to fasten something so that it hangs down.

swal·low (swol′ ō) *n. pl.*, **swal·lows.** a small, thin bird with a forked tail.

sym·bol (sim′ bəl) *n.* sign.

T

tank (tangk) *n.* a large container for holding water.

tas·sel (tas′ əl) *n.* a knot of yarn or hair.

ten·ant (ten′ ənt) *n.* a renter.

ther·mos bot·tle (thur′ məs   bot′ əl) *n.* a bottle in which drinks or other foods can be kept hot or cold for a long time.

PRONUNCIATION KEY
at; āpe; cär; end; mē; it; īce; hot; ōld; fôrk; wood; fo͞ol; oil; out; up; turn; sing; thin; <u>this</u>, hw in white; zh in treasure; ə stands for a in ago, e in taken, i in pencil, o in lemon, u in circus.

throng (thrŏng) *n. pl.,* **throngs.** a crowd; a large number.

tick·ing (tĭk′ ĭng) *n.* a cover for a pillow.

tim·id (tĭm′ ĭd) *adj.* a little frightened; not sure.— **tĭm′ ĭd·ly,** *adv.*

tor·rent (tôr′ ənt) *n. pl.,* **tor·rents.** streams.

twinge (twĭnj) *n.* a sudden pain.

U _____

un·a·ware (ŭn′ ə wer′) *adj.* not noticing; not knowing.

V _____

van·ish (văn′ ĭsh) *v.,* **van·ished.** to go out of sight; to disappear.

ven·ture (vĕn′ chər) *v.* to dare; run the risk of.

vet·er·i·nar·i·an (vĕt′ər ə ner′ē ən) *n.* a doctor or surgeon who treats animals.

vol·un·teer (vŏl′ ən tēr′) *n. pl.,* **vol·un·teers.** a person who agrees to do something freely, not because he or she has to.

W _____

wal·let (wŏl′ ĭt) *n.* a folding purse to hold money or cards.

war·ri·or (wôr′ ē ər) *n.* a soldier.

weird (wērd) *adj.* strange.

wisp (wĭsp) *n. pl.,* **wisps.** a bit; small piece; puff.

wreathe (rēth) *v.,* **wreathed.** to make into a ring.

Y _____

yeast (yēst) *n.* a material used in some kinds of cooking. In baking bread, yeast is used to make the dough rise or swell up.

PRONUNCIATION KEY
at; āpe; cär; end; mē; it; īce; hot; ōld; fôrk; wood; fool; oil; out; up; turn; sing; thin; this, hw in white; zh in treasure; ə stands for a in ago, e in taken, i in pencil, o in lemon, u in circus.

(Acknowledgments continued)

"I Need a Friend" is from I NEED A FRIEND by Sherry Kafka. Text Copyright © 1971 by Sherry Kafka. Reprinted by permission of G. P. Putnam's Sons.

"In the Pitch of the Night" is from BY MYSELF by Lee Bennett Hopkins. Copyright © 1979 by Lee Bennett Hopkins. Reprinted by permission of Curtis Brown, Ltd.

"The Legend of the Bluebonnet" from THE LEGEND OF THE BLUEBONNET by Tomie dePaola. Text and illustrations Copyright © 1983 by Tomie dePaola. Reprinted by permission of G. P. Putnam's Sons and Florence Alexander for the author.

"Losing Your Best Friend" is from LOSING YOUR BEST FRIEND by Corinne Bergstrom. Copyright © 1980. Published by Human Sciences Press, Inc. and reprinted with their permission.

"Make a Mini Igloo" is from "Make a Mini Igloo" by Kimberly Kerin. Adapted/reprinted from the January 1985 issue of Ranger Rick magazine. Copyright © 1986 National Wildlife Federation. By permission of the publisher, National Wildlife Federation.

"Moose Meeting" is from BLUE MOOSE by Manus Pinkwater. Text and illustrations Copyright © 1975 by Manus Pinkwater. Reprinted by permission of Dodd, Mead & Company, Inc.

"My Friend Jacob" is an adaptation of MY FRIEND JACOB by Lucille Clifton. Text Copyright © 1980 by Lucille Clifton. Reprinted by permission of the publisher, E. P. Dutton, a division of New American Library and Curtis Brown, Ltd.

"New Seat, New Friends" is from LUCKY CHARMS & BIRTHDAY WISHES by Christine McDonnell. Copyright © 1984 by Christine McDonnell. Reprinted by permission of Viking Penguin Inc.

"Night Rumbles" is adapted from SEVEN KISSES IN A ROW by Patricia MacLachlan. Copyright © 1983 by Patricia MacLachlan. Reprinted by permission of Harper & Row, Publishers, Inc. and Curtis Brown, Ltd.

"No Dogs Allowed" is an adaptation of "Henry and Ribs" from HENRY HUGGINS by Beverly Cleary. Copyright © 1950 by William Morrow & Company; © renewed 1978 by Beverly Cleary. Adapted by permission of William Morrow & Company.

"Parakeets and Peach Pies" is from PARAKEETS AND PEACH PIES by Kay Smith. Copyright © 1970 by Kay Smith. Reprinted by permission of Scholastic Inc.

"Petey" from PETEY by Tobi Tobias. Text Copyright © 1978 by Tobi Tobias. Reprinted by permission of G. P. Putnam's Sons.

"The Rooster Who Understood Japanese" is adapted from THE ROOSTER WHO UNDERSTOOD JAPANESE by Yoshiko Uchida, Charles Scribner's Sons. Text Copyright © 1976 by Yoshiko Uchida. Reprinted by permission of the author.

"Sam, Bangs and Moonshine" is from SAM, BANGS & MOONSHINE by Evaline Ness. Text and illustrations Copyright © 1966 by Evaline Ness. Reprinted by permission of Henry Holt and Company.

"Snowhouses" from "Snowhouses" by Minnik & Fred Bruemmer. Adapted/reprinted from the January 1985 issue of Ranger Rick magazine. Copyright © 1986 National Wildlife Federation. By permission of the publisher, National Wildlife Federation.

"There Are Rocks in My Socks!" Said the Ox to the Fox is the entire text of "THERE ARE ROCKS IN MY SOCKS!" SAID THE OX TO THE FOX by Patricia Thomas. Copyright © 1979 by Patricia Thomas. By permission of Lothrop, Lee & Shepard Books (A Division of William Morrow & Company).

"Vern" is from BRONZEVILLE BOYS AND GIRLS by Gwendolyn Brooks. Copyright © 1956 by Gwendolyn Brooks Blakely. Reprinted by permission of Harper & Row, Publishers, Inc.

"Weather Is Full of the Nicest Sounds" from I LIKE WEATHER by Aileen Fisher. (Thomas Y. Crowell Company) Copyright © 1963 by Aileen Fisher. Reprinted by permission of Harper & Row, Publishers, Inc. and the author.

ILLUSTRATIONS
Cover: Cheryl Griesbach & Stanley Martucci.
Irv Barnett 270-276; Leslie Bauman 100-101; Mary Young Duarte 26-31; Len Ebert 178-186; Marian Ebert 204-205, 220-226; Allen Eitzen 118-125; Susan Gray 12-23; Jerry Joyner 44-58; Meredith Nemirov 192-203; June Otani 32-41; Anna Rich 59, 142-147; Manny Schongut 131-141; Miriam Schottland 258-268, 269, 274; Bob Shein 232-243; Marti Shohet 128-130, 150-161; Fred Swanson 277-281; Freya Tanz 187, 191; Marsha Winborn 88-99; Wendy Wray 72-82; Lane Yerkes 246-255; Ed Young 104-117.

PHOTOGRAPHY
Pg. 64 (Willinger/Shostal); pg. 65 (Suzanne Szasz/Photo Researchers); pg. 67 (Dennis Purse/Photo Researchers); pg. 69 (William Thompson/Shostal); pg. 70 (Robert Pearcy/Animals, Animals); pg. 118, 120, 121 (David Hiser/Aspen).

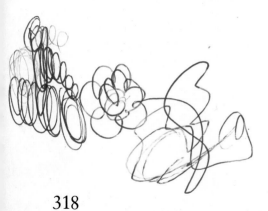

ROCKETS

William K. Durr
Jean M. LePere
Mary Lou Alsin

CONSULTANT: Paul McKee

Houghton Mifflin Company • BOSTON

Atlanta • Dallas • Geneva, Illinois • Hopewell, New Jersey • Palo Alto • Toronto

Contents

Illustrated by: CAROL NICKLAUS
SYLVIA EMRICH • TOM COOKE

Copyright © 1979, 1976 by Houghton Mifflin Company

Printed in the U.S.A.
ISBN: 0-395-26585-1

David

Becky

Andy and Tiger

Jill and Rocket

3

 A is in the 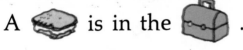 .

And a is in it.

The will go in the .

I will go to in the .

The will go in the .

It will go to .

 I will go to the 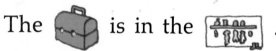 .

The is in the 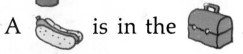 .

It is on a  .

A is in the 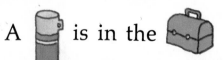 .

A is in the 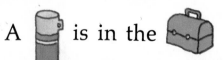 .

And a 🍪 is in it.

 A is not a 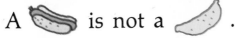 .

A 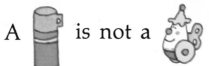 is not a 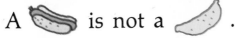 .

A 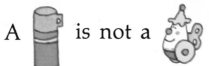 is not a 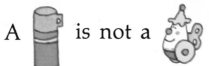 .

 The 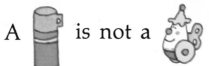 is not in the .

The is not in it.

And the is not in it.

 The will go to you.

 The will go to you.

 The will go on the .

 It will go and go and go.

The  and the

 The is not in the 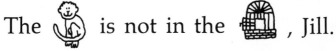, Jill.

It is on the 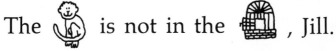.

The will not get the .

 You will not get the .

The is on the 🚌 .

We will help you.

Andy and I will help you get the .

9

The is not on the 🚌 , Jill.

It is not on the 🪑 .

And it is not in the 🌳 .

We will not get the .

 The is on a ⊓ .

You and I will help.

Andy, go and get the .

I will get the a 🍌 .

11

 The 🦁 is in the ▥ .

You will get 🍦 .

The 🦁 will get a 🍌 .

And I will get 🍦 .

Help the Cat

I will get the truck, Andy.

You go and get the cat.

 The cat and I will get in the truck.

You get the truck to go, Andy.

15

 The truck will not go, David.

 Go and get Becky.

She can help you.

 Becky, the truck will not go.

Will you help?

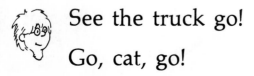 I will help you, Andy.

We can get the truck to go.

And David and the cat will go in it.

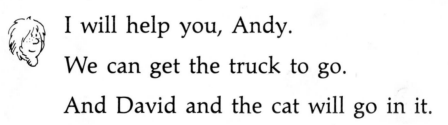 See the truck go!

Go, cat, go!

17

 Come on, Jill.

Come and help David and the cat.

 David is in the truck.

And it will not stop.

 Help! Help!

Stop the truck.

Here we come, David.

We will stop the truck.

We will help you and the cat.

David is here.

He is not in the truck.

And the truck is not here.

 Is the cat here, David?

 The cat!

She is in the truck.

And the truck will not stop.

 I see the truck!

I can not see the cat.

Come here and see the cat.

She is in the truck.

 We can not stop the truck.

And David can not stop it.

 The cat can stop the truck!

22

Come See the Tiger

Come here, David.

Come and see where Rocket is.

He is in here.

He is on TV.

24

 It's not a TV, Andy.
It's a rocket.

 Here we go in the rocket.
Where will we go?

25

David! Andy! Where are you?

 Here we are, Becky.

We are in the rocket.

It's not a rocket.

It's a bus.

Get in.

 Where can we go?

 Stop the bus, Becky.

Tiger is here.

 A tiger!

Can we have a tiger?

Can I have this, Jill?

Come and see a tiger.

 Where is the tiger?

 Andy and David have it.

 We will get in the tiger.

Becky and Jill will not see where we are.

 Stop here.

Help me get this on the truck.

 We have to stop the tiger.

Help me stop it, Becky!

 This tiger will have to go.

 Can we help you with it?

 The tiger will have to go on the truck.

And we can not go with it.

Tigers, Here We Come

 Where can I see a tiger?

 You can see tigers in a zoo.

 Can I go to the zoo?

 You have to go on a bus.

 David and Becky want to go with me.

Can we go on the bus?

 I have to go with you on the bus.

And I can't stop this to go with you.

 You can see a tiger in a zoo.

A bus will go to the zoo.

And I can't go on a bus.

 Here is the zoo bus!

You will not have to get on the bus.

We can see where the bus will go.

 You are a real help, Jill.

 Tigers, here we come!

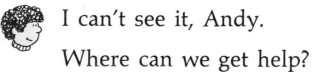 Where is the bus?

Can you see it, David?

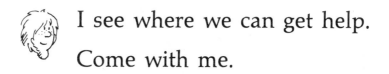 I can't see it, Andy.

Where can we get help?

I see where we can get help.

Come with me.

 Can you help?
We want to go to the zoo.

 Go to the bus stop.
You have to go to the zoo on a bus.

 We can't go on a bus.

You can go to the Bus Stop Zoo.

Can you see it?

 Becky, come and see this.

This is where we want to go.

Come here and see this!

 You come and see this cat, Becky!

 We want to see tigers.

Not cats.

 Can I help you?

 Where is the tiger?
We have come to see a tiger.

 The tigers are in here.
Come with me.

41

 We want to see real tigers.
Not tiger cats.

 I can't have a real tiger here.
You will have to go to a zoo.

 This is a zoo.

You have to have a tiger here.

 It's not a real zoo.

You have to go to the real zoo.

You can go on the bus.

 We can't go on a bus.

We can't get to see a real tiger.

David and the Real Tiger

 We are going to the zoo, David.

We are going on the bus.

We will get to see a real tiger.

Can you come?

 I want to come.

I will have to go and see.

I want to go to the zoo.

Becky and Andy and Jill are going.

You can't go, David.

I want you to come with me.

We are going in the truck.

46

I can't go with you.

I have to go in the truck.

You will get to see a tiger.

And I will not.

 Where is this going?

 It's going to the zoo.

 Can I have help with it?

 You can have help.
He will go with you.

Where are we going?

 We are going where you want to go.

 Are we going to the zoo?

 You will see.

 This is where the tigers are.

 Where are the tigers?

 Is this a real zoo?

 It's a real zoo.

I will see where the tigers are.

50

The tiger is here.

 Is a real tiger on the truck?
Come on, Andy!

 I want to come with you.

David! It's David!

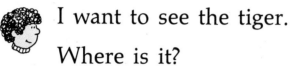 I want to see the tiger.
Where is it?

The tiger is on the truck, David.

52

 Is it a real tiger?

 You have come here with a tiger.

And it's a real tiger.

 Me! With a real tiger!

TIGER and the ROCKET

Where are you going, Tiger?
Are you going to the zoo?

I am not going to the zoo.
You will see where I am going.
Come with me.

Here is where I want to go.

I want to go in this rocket.

Where is it?

You can't go to see this rocket.

I'm going to see this rocket.

I will go on the bus.

You can come to the bus stop with me.

Here is the bus!

I'm going to see the rocket.

 Come here, Tiger.

You can't go in a rocket.

I will have to stop the bus.

Stop, bus! Stop!

The bus will not stop.

Tiger can't go in a real rocket.

I will have to go and stop Tiger.

Where are you going?

I'm going to help Tiger.
I'm going to stop a rocket.

You can't stop a rocket.

I have to stop this rocket.
Tiger is going to get in it.

I will come to help you.

Can you see the rocket?

I can't see the rocket.

And I can't see Tiger.

Come here! Come here!

I can see where the rocket is!

We can go in here.

TO ROCKETS

60

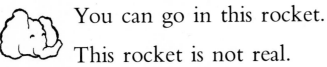 Tiger, we have come to help you.

We are here to stop the rocket.

Where is the rocket?

Here is the rocket I'm going in.

You can go in this rocket.

This rocket is not real.

I can't go in this rocket.
I can't get it to go.

We can help you.
Get in the rocket, Tiger.
We will get it to go.

I will go and go in this rocket.

And I will not stop.

We have to stop.

Come on, Tiger.

I will get you a rocket.

Come on! Come on!

Come and see this.

Come and see Tiger in a rocket!

Here I am.

Come and see me.

I am in a rocket.